BLACK SMOKE

Phil IRVING

M.B.E., C.Eng., F.I.Mech.E., M.S.A.E.(Aus.)

Edited by Col. MURRAY

Publisher:

Research Publications Pty. Ltd.,
418 Canterbury Rd.,
Surrey Hills, Victoria,
Australia.

Printed in Great Britain by HGA Printing Co. and
distributed by:–

Turnpike Bookshop Mail Order,
41 High Street,
Spalding,
Lincolnshire,
England.

National Library of Australia
Cataloguing in Publication Data

Irving, Phil
  Rich Mixture Vol II "Black Smoke"/by
  Phil Irving — Warrandyte,Victoria
  Edited by Col. Murray:
  Research Publications Pty. Ltd.
  418 Canterbury Rd. Surrey Hills, Vic.
  Australia, 1978
  Bibliography.
  ISBN 0 9598398 4 4 First Printing Octavo 1978
  1 Motorcycles 2 Motorcycling I. Murray, Colin, Ed.II. Title
  III Title: "Black Smoke".
  Dewey No. 629 2275.

RESEARCH PUBLICATIONS PTY. LTD.
418 Canterbury Rd. Surrey Hills, Victoria.

First Published in Australia in 1978 by Research Publications
Pty. Ltd.
418 Canterbury Rd., Surrey Hills, Vic. 3127. Australia.
First Printing 1978 136 p octavo.
Second Printing (revised) 1978

Printed in Great Britain by HGA Printing Co.
and distributed by:–

Turnpike Bookshop Mail Order,
41 High Street,
Spalding,
Lincolnshire,
England.

INTRODUCTION

As most of you who read this sort of book will undoubtedly know, running an engine with a rich mixture will usually cause the exhaust pipe to emit black smoke. With black smoke coming after a rich mixture, it would seem obvious (to me anyway) that a follow up book to last year's "Rich Mixture" should be titled "Black Smoke".

Like its forerunner Black Smoke is a collection of articles which were written\ in recent times on a variety of subjects dredged up from a long experience of designing, constructing, riding and writing about motorcycles in Australia and overseas. The majority of articles in this volume first appeared in Motorcycle Action which was edited by Col Murray in Melbourne, but four were printed in more recent times, in Revs Motorcycle News and have been included here with the kind permission of that Sydney magazine's editor.

P. E. Irving

When P.E.I. first suggested we call the second volume of Rich Mixture, "Black Smoke", I baulked at the prospect of seeing that title blaring out from the shelves of a book stall. But after a while I came accept the idea, after all, like the stories enclosed herein it is a typical Irvingism.

The wealth of knowledge and experiences contained in Phil's writings makes this book (and Rich Mixture Volume one) a must for anyone who appreciates engineering in any form, historians who appreciate accurate documentation, mechanically minded folk who wish to learn more, and plain old everyday motorcycle enthusiasts who love a good story told by a master of the trade.

It has been a great honor to have worked with Phil on the Rich Mixture series, I hope these two books foreshadow further writing by Phil with which I will be involved.

Col Murray

Melbourne, May 1978.

Phil Irving M.B.E.,
C.Eng., F.I.Mech.E.,
M.S.A.E.(Aust.)

Other books by Phil Irving

° Tuning for Speed (5th Edition)
° Motorcycle Engineering
° Automobile Engine Tuning
° Two-stroke Power Units
° Rich Mixture Vol. I. A motorcycle miscellany

Col Murray

INDEX

1. SOME EARLY PATENTS

When hunting through some early patent specification files, by chance I came across the original patent covering the geared-crank four-cylinder type of engine used in the Brough Superior "Golden Dream".

This was the British patent No. 135301, granted in November, 1918, to no less a person than Dr. F. W. Lanchester, who, besides manufacturing cars bearing his name, was one of the most eminent engineers engaged in the automobile and aircraft industry in the first quarter of this century.

The illustration is a reproduction of the one published in the patent and shows the close similarity between Lanchester's idea and Brough's reality, and shows that with one pair of cylinders above the other the flow of cooling air round them is better than with any other disposition of four cylinders, except perhaps when idling in neutral when the upper pots are subjected to heat rising from the lower ones.

There was another even more unorthodox four-cylinder machine exhibited at Earl's Court by Wooler in (I think) 1948. Years before, the Wooler possessed a flat-twin engine and unusual plunger type springing fore and aft, while the long slender fuel tank was extended past the steering head and painted yellow, the shape and colour being such that the machine was inevitably nicknamed the "Flying Banana".

The post-war engine had four cylinders in formation across the frame in a similar position to those of the Brough, but instead of two geared crankshafts, there was a central star-shaped member with four arms, each with a short rod connecting it to one piston. This member oscillated on a central pin, and was itself joined by an orthodox con-rod to a crankpin and flywheel assembly lying below the cylinders and offset a little to one side.

There were several good features about this layout. Because the big-ends

7

only moved in an arc instead of a circle, the con-rods could be very short, thus reducing the overall width of the engine and considerably reducing the side-thrust on the pistons. The "under and over" cylinder location provided excellent cooling and the primary forces were in balance, but not being in the same plane, they did generate a rocking couple which could be partly balanced by suitably counter-weighting the flywheel assembly, which constructionally was just the same as a conventional set-up. A disadvantage was that the firing impulses in each side were very unequal, so that for accurate fuel distribution a total of four carburettors would be required.

The complete machine exhibited at the Show looked quite nice, and retained the banana-shaped tank, painted black instead of yellow and with the headlamp mounted in the nose behind a hemispherical glass front.

I happened to be doing a tour around the stands with Harold Taylor, a very outspoken man who though only possessing one leg, was a sidecar trials rider of International calibre. We came to anchor at the Wooler stand, and after surveying the scene for a minute or two, Harold pointed the crutch, which he preferred to a wooden leg, in the general direction of the machine and exclaimed in a voice you could have heard a couple of stands away, "What the hell's that goldfish bowl doing there?", rather to the consternation of an approaching attendant, who tried to pretend not to have heard.

The 1948 Wooler has a transverse "rocking-beam" engine, a rather complicated suspension system and an elongated tank with the headlamp in the nose.

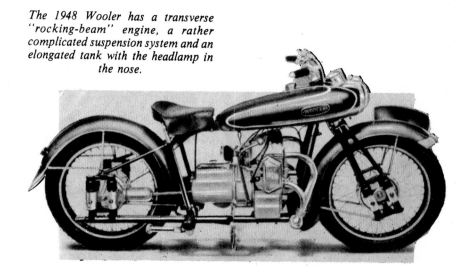

Getting back to Dr. Lanchester and his pioneering work, he took out several patents on two-stroke engines, one of which covers the use of an auxiliary large-diameter short-stroke pumping piston to increase the crankcase breathing, an idea which reappeared subsequently in the DKW.

Dr. F. W. Lanchester's patent for a perfectly balanced four cylinder engine with geared crankshafts, was taken out in 1917.

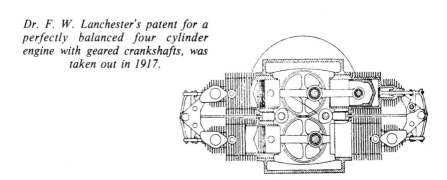

Below: Rear view of the Brough Superior "Gold Dream" engine constructed along the lines of the Lanchester patent.

Lanchester also patented a cylinder with two transfer ports diametrically opposite each other on a line at a right angle to the single exhaust port, while the piston had only a slightly domed crown instead of a deflector. This arrangment was practically the same as the loop-scavenged deflectorless piston engine invented by Schnurrle in Germany twenty years later, and which was the real starting point of the modern high-output two-stroke.

In addition to these, there have been literally hundreds of patents taken out on two-strokes, so many in fact, that virtually every conceivable combination and permutation of pistons, cylinders, valves, crankshafts and crankcases have been propounded at one time or another, but nearly all were unsuccessful or too complicated. Present-day types are mechanically no more complex than the very earliest rudimentary editions which predated the later inventions.

One arrangement which attracted a lot of attention utilized two opposed pistons running in one cylinder, the main feature being that by moving one piston out of phase with the other, the port timing became unsymmetrical and the exhaust port could be closed before the transfer, instead of afterwards as when a single piston is employed. Unsymmetrical port timing gives better low-speed pulling, and much better fuel consumption, because less of the charge is lost through the exhaust. But the power output is less for reasons which are a trifle too complicated to deal with here.

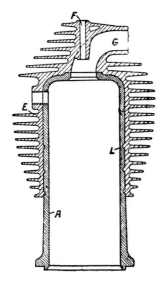

A bi-metal four-stroke cylinder with a fixed head and a cast-on aluminium jacket was patented by the Villiers company in 1917.

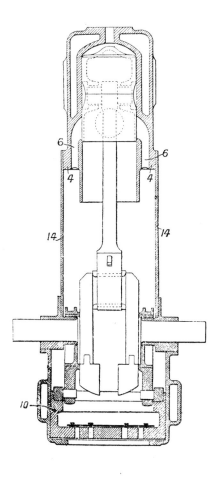

Walter Kaarden, the East German citizen who developed the disc-valved MZ into a racewinner and indirectly helped the Japanese on to the right track, tried out a design with two pistons and two crankshafts which gave very little power, but on the economy side we developed a twin-cylinder double-crankshaft engine at the Vincent Co. intended for long-range air-sea rescue work which could propel a 30 foot (9 metres) life-boat for over 1000 miles on 50 gallons (227 litres) of petrol. This was more than twice as far as any contemporary two or four-stroke engine could achieve.

A surprising amount of thought was put into light-weight cylinders in the early days. Granville Bradshaw, the designer of the A.B.C. motorcycle and aeroplane engines, patented a system of turning thin fins on a solid billet of steel, and then copper plating them for better heat conduction.

11

The Villiers Engine Co. in Wolverhampton which was a pioneer maker of small two-strokes, must also have dabbled with four-strokes because a patent taken out by the company in 1917 describes an iron cylinder with an integral head containing two valve seats around which was cast a finned aluminium jacket that also formed the inlet and exhaust ports.

Several other patents for cast-on aluminium jackets were also granted to other people but this construction entails a specialised foundry technique and it was not until nearly 20 years later that this type of bi-metal cylinder became a commercial proposition.

After a while it in turn was superseded by bored-out jackets fitted with press-fit liners which are now virtually standard items of specification.

By no means were all these odd patents useful. Some were obviously crackpot ideas not worth powder and shot and others were the outcome of wrong thinking. For instance, S. L. Bailey, an Australian who designed some extremely successful Douglas racing engines patented the use of exhaust valve guides which fitted very loosely in the head and were located by a spherical collar. The idea was to permit the head to line up accurately with the seat irrespective of thermal distortions, but in practice it would inevitably lead to overheated or burnt valves.

2. FADS AND FASHIONS

In the days when masculine clothing used to be restrained in cut and sombre in color and nobody would have dreamed of putting on jeans before going to a dinner party, the variety of women's fashions from hats down to shoes and the rapidity with which the styles came and went was frequently a cause of amusement,except of course to the rag trade which made a good thing out of it.

Motorcyclists or at least some sections of that community, are nearly as bad a women, going wild over some design feature or accessory until it becomes a fashion. After a while, if the item concerned is of no practical use and was simply a fad, it fades out and another gimmick takes its place.

I can recall a time when a very low saddle height was considered to be so desirable that frames like the Cotton and Chater-Lea were designed with straight top tubes expressely to keep the saddle height down. Almost every catalogue description included the phrase "very low riding position," even if infact is was not.

It became a cult in Victoria to take the saddle off and sit on a thin cushion unless you wanted to demonstrate your toughness and just sat directly on the frame tubes. Cushion or not, this provided the acme of discomfort, partly because the knees were folded up so much that the legs could support very little of the rider's weight. Also it could absolutely ruin the handling as I discovered when stupidly trying out the scheme on a 350 AJS using a cushion as a concession to my physical frailty.

Two-port heads and upswept exhaust pipes were both popular in the 1930's, often to the detriment of performance and clothing.

On sandy surfaces, this machine, which used to handle reasonably well, became almost dangerously prone to skidding sideways. Maintaining a straight course required continual steering corrections which ceased to be necessary after the saddle had been replaced.

The fashion died out after a few months and also manufacturers drew away from the ultra-low saddle position and reverted to a more sensible height.

Another pointless fashion was the fitting of upswept trials-type exhaust systems to touring machines when pillion equipment was also supplied and used.

These button-hook pipes were frequently listed as optional equipment supplied at a small extra charge but they became so popular even with those who never considered riding in trials that several factories fitted them as standard, low pipes then becoming optional.

At about this period, twin exhaust port heads were the "in" thing and as it was almost impossible to tuck a pair of high silencers in very closely, burnt stockings or legs became almost an occupational disease amongst pillion passengers. Heat shields on the pipes helped a little but not much as they also increased the width, so upswept pipes gradually fell from favour.

14

Nowadays there is a strong tendency to turn the exhaust system into a styling feature with a separate pipe and megaphone shaped silencer for each cylinder, resulting in a blatant display of shining chrome and a large bill for repairs in the event of a bingle.

Twin exhaust ports, which happily are no longer with us except on historical machines, were one of the worst design features ever adopted on four-strokes. They came into fashion after Herbert le Vack constructed a head for his racing JAP engine with one port in the usual position and another jutting out sideways. This scheme might have helped on the Brooklands track where regulation — pattern silencers had to be fitted, noise abatement being by no means a new-fangled idea.

With two pipes Le Vack could use two "Brooklands cans" as the silencers were called, and maybe gained some benefit, but other features embodied in the engine could have been really responsible for its success.

Be that as it may, the fashion caught on and most manufacturers merely added a second port to an existing single-port head. The net result was usually to knock a lot off the performance besides creating trouble with overheating and burning of exhaust valves due to the great increase in the port area exposed to heat.

Even Velocettes bowed to the dictate of fashion by producing the KTP, which apart from having coil ignition was basically the same as the overhead camshaft model K except for the twin-port head. This was probably the only flop the Hall Green factory ever built and the best way to get a respectable performance from it was to block up the near-side port with a shaped filler.

Nevertheless, popular demand was such that many factories retained this costly method of spoiling an engine's performance for several years although it disappeared very quickly from the racing scene.

Four-valve heads as on the Rudge or Ariel were differently placed as each exhaust valve had its own single port and pipe, these being well splayed out so that the area between them could be adequately cooled.

One invention which started as a fashion and became a necessity was the positive-stop foot change, devised, as were so many valuable ideas, by the now despised British industry in the person of Harold Willis who also invented the long racing saddle which he termed the "Loch Ness Monster". This was the ancestor of present-day seating accommodation.

In a way, scooters were only a fashion even though it lasted for several years. Plenty of scooters had been made with little or no sales success until the Lambretta appeared and just why a device so ugly and awkward looking become a rage almost overnight, is something of a mystery.

Of the many designs which followed some caught on and some did not, but at one period there were three or four million scooters on the roads in Europe. Then the demand tapered off almost to zero and the type is now virtually extinct.

However, while they lasted, scooters produced some minor fashions of their own, such as tall fake aerials sticking up at the stern with an imitation foxtail atop, or if you were a continental, a string of little colored pennants.

Handlebars have been the subject of many crazes, differing from country to country. For years Americans preferred the cow-horn variety giving a riding position similar to the "sit up and beg" shape, which in England gave way to the flat sports bar.

A few years back. English coffee-bar cowboys went overboard for clip-on bars fastened to the forks so low down that the riding position was extremely uncomfortable. But for some reasons, human beings will put up with any sort of discomfort rather than be out of fashion — like wearing narrow shoes and enduring the resulting corns.

Strangely enough, in Australia the trend was in the opposite direction, accessory shops marketing bars with the grips raised higher and higher until the repellent "ape-hanger" shape developed.

Some dealers quite rightly refused to retail these exaggerated shapes on the grounds that they could slip too easily in the clamps and also because they afford less accuracy of control than the standard shape of bars.

Above: The positive stop footchange invented by Harold Willis set a fashion which became universal. This picture shows its original form in 1932.

Right: Turning the exhaust system into a styling feature is a heavy and expensive feature found mostly on Japanese machines — but occasionally the Europeans found the need to keep pace with the trend.

Opposite page: The sooner this crazy fad vanishes from the face of the earth, the better.

If there is any coherent thought about it all except a desire to attract attention, it is difficult to understand this rage to twist bars into odd shapes such as bringing the grips to shoulder height, but very close together and almost touching the rider's chest. This contortion gives, in effect, tiller steering instead of the balanced push and pull effect of normal bars. But like the dangling dolls sometimes to be seen in car windscreens, they at least provide an indication of the mentality of the man at the helm.

Disc brakes are an example of a valuable feature which can be over-emphasised by fashion.

The main advantage of a disc over a drum is its ability to retain its power after many savage applications at racing speeds. For normal road use where this treatment is unusual and unnecessary, a well-designed drum brake is just as effective and if often sweeter in action.

Nevertheless, running around the street you can see models of very modest performance lugging along a set of discs big enough to stop a full size motor car. This not only involves the rider in unecessary expense but may well lead to his undoing on a slippery surface where an overbraked machine can become a source of danger.

The economic value of producing disc brakes may or may not be a determining factor as to their popular use these days, but fitting discs to small capacity commuters is definitely a case of pandering to a fad, or more correctly pandering to the public which likes to be trendy.

3. RIDING STYLES

Riding styles are like fashions in clothes; they change over the years, but not always for the better.

Although the "Brooklands crouch", with the rider lying flat along the tank was the accepted thing for early track-racing, it did not come into general use for road-racing for many years. In fact as late as 1922 the single-cylinder Indian which Freddy Dixon rode in the Senior T.T. was equipped like a real touring machine with footboards, and of all things, a back-rest which prevented him from doing much wind-cheating.

Then riders like Charlie Dobson started to slide back on to their pillion seats to get down a bit lower, and this led to the previously mentioned invention by Harold Willis of what he called the "Loch Ness Monster" a combined saddle and pillion seat which he patented. For a while it was used exclusively on Velocettes, then Willis assigned the patent to Dunlot's, who had made the original models, and after that anybody could use it, and many people did.

Stanley Woods, who was a rider of championship calibre in those days, would get well down out of the wind most of the time, but always preferred to sit up when approaching and rounding a slowish corner. This habit gave onlookers the impression that he was not cornering very fast, but he was just as quick, maybe quicker, than anyone else, and moreover, he seldom fell off.

His reasons for sitting up were two-fold: one was that he felt more in command of the ship, and the other was that using air-resistance as a brake took a lot of the strain off the stoppers which were not quite as good then as they are now. There must have been a lot in what Woods said, because he could lap nearly as fast in the wet or foggy conditions as in the dry, and he rarely had trouble with brakes, even though slower riders were grumbling about brake-fade especially at the end of long down-hill sections.

It has often occurred to me that a more upright riding position would be better on tight short-distance circuits than a really flat-down attitude, and in fact this has been demonstrated fairly clearly in production races.

When discussing riding styles with Maurice Quincey and some other T.T. riders, there was general agreement that in his heyday, Geoff Duke was easily the most polished and effortless performer we had ever seen. He cut his racing teeth on the T.T. circuit in the Isle of Man winning the Manx G.P., the Senior Clubman's race, and then two Senior International T.T.'s in succession, and of course, went on to become a multiple World Champion.

The American version of what became known as the "Brooklands Crouch".

Accustomed to riding on long fast circuits, he would settle down into his characteristic position immediately after climbing on board at the start and thereafter hardly moved a muscle, except for operating the controls or to sit up just a little in the twisty bits.

Having determined the fastest and safest line on the corners in practice, he would follow it faithfully for lap after lap, except when forced to circumnavigate a slower opponent.

Quincey shared my objections to the ungainly knee-out theory introduced by Mike Hailwood, who while perhaps faster than Duke, was never quite so tidy. The theory is that by transferring some of the weight to the inside of the corner, you can get around faster without increasing the banking angle of the machine and while this is true to some extent, there is no point in the idea unless the machine is already at its maximum safe angle of lean. Yet one sees quite mediocre performers sticking their knees out, just because the top-liners do it.

Quincey's objection was that when a rider's knee cap is almost skimming the ground, it is not only liable to painful and possibly permanent injury, but also there is a grave risk of having the foot knocked off the footrest, with consequent lost of control, and a chance of a pile-up involving other riders.

Whatever one's views about the style may be, there is no doubt that Quincey had a valid point. When it comes to riding with both knees out, the whole exercise just becomes silly.

Multiple Australian champion Ken Blake maintains that he and other "slightly built" jockeys need to hang off the bigger, heavier bikes to get them round corners. He may have a point but the practice appears to be used more as pure "style" rather than for practical reasons by many riders.

Another thing which came under discussion was monowheeling down the straight, in full view of the cash customers and any photographers who happen to be within view-finder range. After all, since small boys on half-pint minibikes can easily duplicate the star performer's efforts in this direction, it does not necessarily indicate enormous power, but rather that the weight distribution and the aerodynamics of the racing machine are at fault.

As far as speed is concerned, you will never see a picture of a record-breaker rushing along on its hind legs, except maybe for a short distance following a standing start. The reason is that it can be driven faster with both wheels on the ground than with the front wheel up in the air, so holding a wheelie all the way past the grandstand when well ahead of the field is nothing less than what theatre-goers would dismiss as "playing to the gallery". Tricks of this nature, like standing on the saddle, sitting back to front, or jumping over a row of cars, should be confined to the infield, where a misjudgement will hurt nobody but the performer, and the acts can be judged by the spectators for what they are — examples of riding which however skilful or daring, have no place in the serious business of racing, or for that matter, ordinary riding on the road.

21

Two contrasting road race riding styles, one, that of Bob Rosenthal, (right) in the regrettable "knees-everywhere" style and the other, a picture of neatness from Ray Quincey (above).

In that last phrase lies one of the dangers. Young followers of any sport are apt to regard the top men with a considerable amount of hero-worship, and naturally tend to emulate their behavior and actions. There are enough crack-brained riders around already to be a menace to themselves and others without them indulging in unofficial one-wheel contests on the highway. It is pretty certain that if observed by the arm of the law, such behaviour would merit a charge of dangerous or careless riding which would be very hard to explain away to an unsympathetic magistrate. And it would be no bad thing if the same procedure was followed by stewards at race meetings before the practice spreads from one or two leading riders right down to the back-markers who also want a slice of publicity.

Something which the sidecar boys have not got around to yet is coming down the straight with the chair-wheel air-borne, not that this would be an easy task with today's low-slung outfits. I used to do a bit of this myself, and on one occasion managed to convince a Court that, despite what the policeman said, the outfit was under control. Proficiency in the art also enabled me to finish a Club trial on time, with the detached sidecar wheel in the chair, and the passenger on the pillion for three miles but that, as Kipling said, is another story.

4. CORNERING CLEARANCE

O ne of the most disconcerting things that can happen when testing a new model, or even when trundling a familiar machine smartly along strange roads with unexpected sharp bends, is to find that you cannot get around a corner because some projecting part of the machine comes into contact with the road before the appropriate banking angle is reached. If this happens when some other vehicle coming the opposite way prevents you from running wide, everyone concerned is likely to be in real trouble. The moral is never to take chances on corners even on machines which you do know well.

Speed as such is not necessarily a contributing factor. On occasions in traffic it may be necessary to do some violent swervery to avoid a collision even at quite a low speed, but severe grounding when the bike is heeled over smartly to one side may make your well-intentioned efforts useless.

Providing enough cornering clearance for safety even under racing conditions is not difficult with a narrow engine or gearbox, the areas most likely to touch then being the footrests or the exhaust system.

Years ago, most designers adopted a rule stipulating that no part of the machinery should project beyond two imaginary surfaces extending upwards on both sides at 45 degrees, and tangential to the tyre walls when both wheels were at the full upward travel of their suspensions, this angle being chosen because it corresponds approximately to the limit of adhesion of the average tyre on a level surface such as dry bitumen. However, road surfaces are rarely either flat or level, and sometimes are not dry, and even at this angle, grounding may occur through hitting a bump while the wheels are traversing a hollow.

It seems that the time-honored rule is not always followed on modern

The Laverda 750's "balancer" pipe is the first thing to scrape on coernering. This photo shows the bike in almost racing conditions on a race track. In normal road riding scraping the pipe, except in extreme circumstances, would not occur. The same applies to the BMWs (below). Racing this machine requires the rider to keep in mind the vulnerability of the rocker covers.

touring machines, even though some are as fast as real racers used to be. Even the 45 degrees angle is insufficient with modern tyre compounds which provide a much greater grip on dry surfaces than ordinary rubber does.

Road testers often find that severe grounding occurs even when they are not trying to get round corners as fast as possible. This is a potentially dangerous defect for which there is no valid excuse, and has been made more prevalent by employing very wide transverse engines and bulky exhaust systems made more for show than for utility.

An interesting piece of equipment was used by machine examiners at the TT to ensure that riders do not unwittingly endanger themselves or others. This is a wooden contrivance, with a central channel for the tyres and two side wings extending upwards at 45 degrees just like the imaginary planes mentioned earlier. Each machine was wheeled through, and if any part touched the wings while the machine was held vertical, it was promptly rejected and not finally accepted as being fit for racing until suitable modifications enabled it to pass the test.

This seems to be an admirable idea which could well be adopted here, especially for production racing. But for it to be of real value, the machine should either be pulled down hard on the front and rear springs, or at least loaded with a full tank of fuel, plus the rider or an equivalent weight. Alternatively, the floor of the channel could be lowered by an amount equal to the travel of the suspension.

The grounding problem involves two dimensions, height and width. Parts such as the legs of a central stand which are close to the road must be very narrow, a point which is often disregarded, while parts which are unavoidably wide, such as footrests, clutch covers or electrical equipment carried on the end of a transverse crankshaft, must be kept high off the ground.

Although this is a subject which **BMW** enthusiasts prefer not to be openly discussed, the extreme width of a big transverse-twin has always presented a problem operating against its success in solo racing. In order to keep the rocker boxes from grounding too easily and limiting the cornering speed, the engine has to be placed so high that the handling suffers when flapping the model through a succession of curves at high velocity. In fact, the only solo rider who really shone on a **BMW** was Walter Zeller, a German factory rider who had never ridden anything else.

It has always seemed strange to me that the Munich factory did not compromise with its principles and incline the cylinders upwards at 8 degrees or so, which would provide 1½ inches (3.75cm) more clearance. The mechanical balance would be nearly as perfect as it is now, and a small alteration to the crankshaft would provide equal firing intervals, if such a feature was thought to be worth struggling for.

In off-road conditions, a bike can often go down nearly flat on its side, but a skilful rider will be able to recover from this position provided that nothing digs into the ground and brings the proceedings to a halt. For that reason, trail and scramble models are very high-built, and have narrow single-cylinder engines with raised exhaust systems, and everthing else either tucked in closely or able to fold up out of the way. Unfortunately, these precautions do not always provide a very comfortable riding position, but as trailriding is not a very restful pastime anyway, comfort is of less importance than suitability for the job in hand.

5. TWIST-GRIP THROTTLE CONTROL

T hrottle control by twist-grip is one of those items which has become so much a part of the accepted order of things that it is rarely the subject of discussion, but it is also one of the few mechanical devices which became simpler through continuous development instead of more complicated.

Exactly when the idea of the twist-grip first originated is very difficult to say. There is one early example in a museum at Canterbury, Kent, in which a cord wrapped round the grip passed over pulleys to apply the rear brake of a sort of oversized scooter built mainly of wood at least a century ago, but not being actually a throttle control it is somewhat outside the scope of this article. The idea of twisting the grip to open the throttle became almost a standard fitting on American motorcyles around the turn of the century, and certainly before it came into use in England or on the Continent. Instead of the flexible Bowden cable which was then in its infancy, and little-known in America, a cable very similar to the type still employed for choke controls on cars was used. This has a fairly stiff spirally wound outer casing with a single strand of piano-wire sliding within, and although it cannot be carried round sharp corners, it is able to operate as a push-pull cable and thus can be used without a return spring.

The American-style twist grip rotating on the outside of the handle-bar was connected to some concealed mechanism inside the bar in order to provide a straight pull on the inner wire. The cable emerged from the bar through a hole close to the steering head, the whole arrangement being very tidy although the hole sometimes formed the starting point of a fatigue crack.

English and Continental factories retained lever control using Bowden wire and return springs in the carburettors for many years until deciding to adopt twist-grips, while still retaining Bowden cables which being much more flexible than piano-wire could be installed more easily with sharper bends.

29

Some of the early patterns designed to provide a straight pull with the cable either inside or outside the handle-bar were fairly deplorable. They were lacking in freedom and nicety of movement due to the use of coarse-pitch spiral slot and peg to convert rotary into linear motion, which is the sort of mechanism that can easily lock up if there is any excess friction or load on the cable.

Most motorcycle racing at this period took place on artificial circuits such as Brooklands, where once you got into top gear you stayed there, and many speed-men preferred lever control partly because it lessened the strain on the wrist, and partly because once the lever was in the full-speed-ahead position

The throttle and ignition advance were both controlled by twistgrips on the very "clean" bars of this Indian "Powerplus".

there was less tendency to nudge it back a little, either inadverdently or on purpose. Also, in the long-distance record attempts which were made almost once a week, a lever would remain where it was put and the throttle would not be subjected to involuntary jiggling movements over the bumps.

Velocette was rather slow in adopting the twist grip partly because Harold Willis, who was the Development Engineer as well as a "works" T.T. rider, preferred lever control and retained it on all his racing machines until he retired in 1932. What Velo. then did was to devise a very simple grip which operated a push-pull cable, formed by winding a wire around an ordinary Bowden inner wire and running this in a large-bore outer cable which was anchored at both ends, thereby making the return spring unnecessary. The action was extremely light — in fact a little too light as you could not tell by feel what position the throttle was in. Another defect of this system was that if the throttle slide or the cable became jammed or stiff and force was applied to wind back the grip, the exposed upper end of the inner wire was liable to fold up into a loop and effectively prevent throttle closure. Not a common occurrence, but a trifle disturbing when it did happen.

During a once-fashionable cult for clean bars, the lefthand grip was sometimes utilized to advance or retard the ignition, but this was a bad idea because it was so easy for an inexperienced rider to run with the spark partially or fully retarded without being conscious of it, with an adverse effect of the fuel consumption, and also causing the engine to overheat. Fortunately, this fad only lasted for a year or so. Amal, Doherty and one or two smaller English accessory makers marketed several patented grips and then started to pinch each other's ideas as well. This led to a law-suit over infringement of patent rights costing the companies several thousand pounds in legal fees, which was simply money down the drain, because all the patents were finally declared to be invalid and from that time on anyone who wanted to get into the twist-grip business was free to do so.

The original Bowden inner cable was made from a number of fine spiral-wound, hard-drawn steel wires, and if cut through would promptly unwind itself unless the cutting area was thoroughly tinned with solder in advance. Then a non-fraying grade was produced which did not unravel and being slightly softer did not object to being repeatedly bent and straightened. It could be used without the likelihood of early failure in the cotton-reel type of grip from which the cable emerged at right angles to the bar. This type was the forerunner of nearly all the grips used today, and is easily the least complicated. Being very free in action, the throttle can be made self-closing for competition work so the engine is automatically shut off in the event of a fall, but holding the throttle open against even a moderately strong spring can become very tiring on a long journey. To overcome this, a device is sometimes incorporated which can be adjusted to give precisely the right amount of friction to suit individual taste.

Too much friction anywhere in the control system tends to give the impression that the engine has lost its edge and a few minutes spent in making sure that the cable is working freely and adjusting the grip correctly often has a surprisingly effective result. On the other hand, quick-action grips do not help in getting good fuel economy, as there is a tendency to over-open the throttle for accelleration and then to close it back a little. Many years ago I discarded the lever control on my "big port" A.J.S. in favour of a quick-action Binks push-pull grip, and although this made the bike much more responsive, it dropped the petrol mileage from about 90 m.p.g. down to about 75. This was a serious matter when a good consumption was something to boast about, and petrol was much more expensive in relation to wages than it is today.

As it was not unknown for a rider to pull the end off a throttle cable in a desperate attempt to wring a few more knots out of an engine which was already on full bore, Amal produced a grip with a maximum-travel stop which could be adjusted so that the cable could not be over-stressed, but this valuable little refinement seems to have disappeared and throttle cables still occasionally break. Another refinement is the twin-cable grip for use with dual carburettors. A single-cable model can be modified without much trouble beyond replacing the existing cable abutment with another which takes two cables side by side and making the groove in the hand-piece wide enough for two inner wires which can be sweated into a single nipple.

6. COMPRESSION RATIOS

N ext to the bore, stroke and capacity (or if you like, swept volume or displacement), the most commonly quoted feature of any engine is the compression ratio, which in kindergarten terms is an indication of how tightly the fuel and air mixture is squeezed into a small space by the rising piston before the power stoke.

The effect of compressing the mixture is to speed up the combustion process so that burning is completed in about 20 degrees of crank rotation, and although this action is commonly referred to as an "explosion", in actual fact it is not a true explosion but an extremely rapid passage of flame which starts at the plug and spreads throughout the combustion chamber. In a badly designed cylinder, the last part of the charge still to be burnt does sometimes explode, giving rise to a knocking or "pinking" noise. But this bad condition which plagued early engineers, has been very nearly eradicated, partly by better design, and partly by better fuels. These developments have enabled the usable ratio for road four-strokes to go from about 4 to 1 up to 8 or 9 to 1, while racing engines go up to 12 to 1 on high octane petrol.

Confusion sometimes exists about how the ratio is determined. It is not, as is sometimes thought, the relation between the volume displaced or swept by the piston and the volume of the combusion space at top dead centre, but the relation between the whole interior volume (swept volume plus head volume) and the head volume. Using the erroneous system gives a figure one ratio less than it should be. If the head volume of a 250cc cylinder is 25cc the C.R. is 11 to 1, not 10 to 1. Even then, the correct figure is only a theoretical value, and assumes that the cylinder is completely full at b.d.c., and that compression starts immediately the piston commences to rise.

The time-honored method of finding the clearance volume by measuring the amount of liquid poured into the head.

Only rarely would these two factors occur simultaneously, for at low speeds, true compression does not commence until the inlet valve shuts, which is anything from 45 to 85 degrees, after b.d.c. At higher speeds, the cylinder may be well below atmospheric pressure at the start of the stroke, but at still higher speeds, the pressure may be above atmospheric at this point if the lengths of the inlet and exhaust systems are correctly proportioned to utilize ram and wave effects to the full. Therefore, just knowing what the measured ratio happens to be is, as mentioned earlier, not much more than a very rough indication of the final compression pressure. This is also modified to some degree by the temperature of the combustion chamber walls and piston crown. The hotter these surfaces are, the higher the final pressure will be, and when using cool-running alcohol blends, the theoretical pressure is appreciable lower than with petrol, as shown in the accompanying graph. Aluminium heads have the same sort of effect, when compared to those made of lamp-post metal.

So far we have only been considering four-strokes. Until comparatively recently, two-stroke compressions were calculated in exactly the same way, and then someone in Germany trotted out the theory that as compression could not start until the exhaust port was closed, the whole swept volume of the cylinder should not be used, but only the volume swept after port-closure by which time the piston is well up to the stroke. This gives a much lower figure than that derived from the conventional method, and there seems to be little merit in the idea. The result is meaningless unless the port height is

34

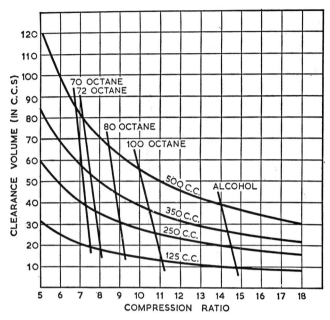

Chart giving the approximate clearance volume required for the different fuels in various cylinder sizes.

known. Also, on this system any modification to port height will alter the calculated compression ratio, which is about as illogical as saying that altering the valve timing would alter the compression ratio of a four-stroke. Nevertheless, many makers have adopted the idea, without actually saying so, although Suzuki refer in their workshop manuals to the "corrected" compression ratio, which presumably means what we have just been talking about. Other makers stick to the old method, and a good deal of confusion is caused by the co-existence of both systems, because a machine of one make will be quoted has having a ratio of say 6.4 to 1, while a rival model of different make but similar performance will be credited with 12 to 1 or thereabouts.

Sometimes the word "uncorrected" added to the data panel just makes matters more obscure. On the whole, it would be very much bettter if the ratio was not mentioned at all, and the specification just stated the compression volume, leaving the owner to work the ratio out for himself. It would also give machine examiners a clear-cut figure for use when determining the eligibility or otherwise of an alleged "production" engine.

35

A well-designed two-stroke can utilize a higher ratio than a four-stroke for a couple of reasons. One is that in the absence of valves no pockets are required in the piston crown and the whole combustion space can be of a very favourable shape. And the other is that the two-stroke volumetric efficiency is lower so that the compression pressure is less for any given ratio.

The EMC, which I worked on with Dr. Ehrlich in 1959, ran at 19 to 1, and developed 29 b.h.p. at 10,500 r.p.m. or about the same as the contemporary M.Z., whereas 12 to 1 would be just about the limit in a four-stroke on the petrol officially supplied at the time.

Raising the ratio works on the law of diminishing returns. You just cannot go on boosting it up regardless, because the gain in power becomes less and less until a figure is reached above which no further gain in power can be obtained. In a four-stroke this is partly because with inclined valves and a high dome on the piston, the combustion chamber becomes shaped like an orange-peel and this is not conducive to good burning and high power. Meanwhile, although the increase in power for each rise in ratio becomes less, the explosion pressures continually become higher, being of the order of 800 p.s.i. at 8 to 1, but rising to round 1200 p.s.i. at 12 to 1, and even higher if occasional detonation is occurring. This naturally puts a much greater strain on the whole structure and may lead to blown head-gaskets, caved-in piston crowns, or in the case of a vintage model with a flanged cylinder base, a danger that the cylinder will break off above the flange. It was to avoid this calamity that the K.T.T. base flange was doubled in thickness in 1931 after failures had occurred when running on alcohol at about 11 to 1. Later on, the barrel flange was discarded and long bolts running right through to the head were employed. Applying this reasoning in reverse, it is not advisable to reduce the flange thickness of an old model if it is subsequently to be driven hard.

High compression also has a beneficial effect on fuel economy, especially at part throttle. If a fuel crisis strikes again it is worth bumping up the ratio to about 10 to 1 or at least to a point where the engine exhibits audible signs of distress at full throttle, and either limit the twist grip travel to about half-throttle or else use your throttle hand with considerable restraint to avoid pinking.

7. CYLINDER FINS

Every internal-combustion engine operates by converting heat energy into mechanical work, but although better than in some other varieties of engine such as turbines or steam plants, the conversion process is not very efficient.

Less than one-third of the heat energy is transformed into power at the crankshaft, the rest being absorbed by the combustion-chamber and cylinder walls or is rejected on the exhaust stroke.

In a two-stroke, expecially one designed for high specific output at high r.p.m. a certain amount of fresh mixture excapes into the exhaust system without being burnt. But while this is a cause of inefficiency and contributes to the excessively high consumption for which this type of engine has become notorious, it does not add to the amount of heat absorbed by the cylinder.

As a rough approximation, this heat is about equivalent to the quantity turned into power, so if an engine is developing 30 b.h.p. equal to 22 kilowatts of electrical energy, the heat absorbed by the cylinder would be at least 22kw. or the same as that emitted by 22 one-bar electric fires — enough to keep a large house comfortable warm. This heat has to be got rid of somehow, otherwise the engine would overheat and seize in a short space of time, and the simplest method is to increase the area available for radiation by adding fins to all the hot areas.

History does not reveal who first thought of this idea, but the earliest air-cooled engines were very scantily finned, possibly because at the time not many foundries were able to cast deep fins satisfactorily. However, these rudimentary fins worked well enough to cope with the small power outputs of the period, except on hills or with following winds. Involuntary stops to let the engine cool off were recognized by pioneer motorcyclists being part of the game.

Sidevalve and two-stroke engines were especially prone to losing power or even seizing because of the extra heat given up to the port walls while the irregular sections caused barrel distortion and local hot spots. J. L. Norton appreciated this defect and designed his I6H model with an air space between the exhaust port and the barrel, a feature which contributed greatly to the success of this engine.

It would actually have been better also to angle the port out to the side in the fashion of several contemporary American machines but the current thinking was to tuck everything close in and out of harm's way in the likely event of a fall.

In the early days most racing took place on closed circuits and there was no insistence on using petrol; when alcohol fuels were employed, the cool running they provided enabled lightly-finned engines to keep going for hours at a stretch. The original KTT Velo., for instance, covered just over 100 miles in one hour and also averaged over 78m.p.h. for 12 hours on the Montlhery track in France, in 1928, using an alcohol blend called R.D.1.

It was not until "dope" was prohibited in road racing that attention to cooling became imperative. From 1930 onwards fins gradually increased in size, the Velo for example, going in six years from six inches to over 10 inches in diameter (15cm-25cm). On the "works" racing engines the fins were even wider and almost square instead of being circular. The great width was not so much to provide more area, as to move the fin tips out into the effective air stream. Experiments with an air speed indicator and a Pitot head placed in various localities, had shown that at high speed, the air behind the front wheel was almost stagnant.

Very deep closely pitched fins are not easy to cast in iron and their weight is undesirable but the position was changed by re-introducing an idea patented by S. S. Guy in England in 1918, presumably for aircraft engines. This consisted of casting an aluminium sleeve around a plain cylinder and the patent included a detachable head with light alloy fins cast around an iron skull.

Left: Radial fins are now very common in two-stroke engines. On this Minarelli engine they are joined together by "stiffeners".

Below: The head and barrel fins on the 1909 1000cc J.A.P. V-twin are very scanty, but were representative of the period. This engine is still used in Vintage rallies in Victoria.

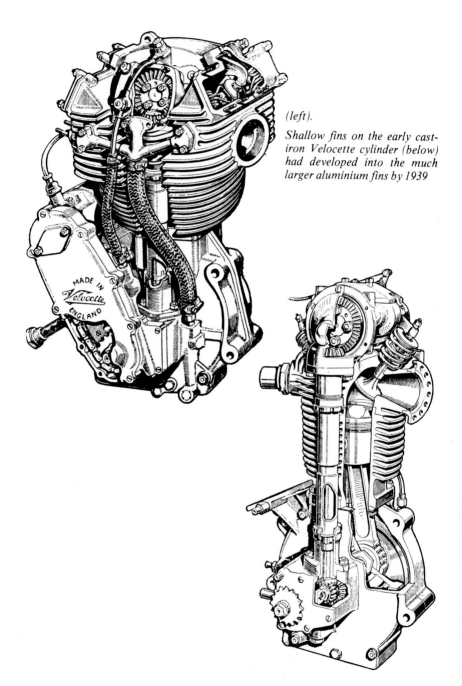

(left).

Shallow fins on the early cast-iron Velocette cylinder (below) had developed into the much larger aluminium fins by 1939

Neat conventional finning on the Gold Star B.S.A. The push-rods are enclosed in a tunnel, cast integrally with the aluminium jacket.

Aluminium is better in this regard than iron because it has twice the thermal conductivity, is less than half the weight and can be cast in very thin sections, but unfortunately a special foundry technique is required to obtain satisfactory components. The sand mould must be thoroughly dry and the iron barrel must be heated, placed in the mould and the aluminium poured in immediately, otherwise condensation occurs and the subsequent evolution of steam creates blow holes or areas of separation between the jacket and cylinder.

The Idoson Cylinder Co. in Smethwick, made most of the bi-metal barrels for the trade under the direction of Harry Taft who for some years raced an Excelsior "Manxman" with good effect. He was prepared to cut up any number of barrels without charge to the customer to detect faults and improve the technique. He eventually decided that the best results were obtained if the iron cylinder had a large number of triangular grooves cast in its surface.

As aluminium has twice the thermal expansion of iron it therefore tends to separate at a high temperature, but as the barrel is always the hotter of the two, separation is not a serious matter. The skull in bimetal heads was made of aluminium — bronze as this has nearly the same thermal expansion as aluminium and close contact is maintained at almost any temperature.

41

A better and simpler solution to the barrel problem was to fit a fully machined, thin iron liner into an accurately bored light-alloy jacket shrunk on with sufficient interference to avoid separation at working temperature. The resulting cylinder was half the weight of the solid iron one with equivalent fins. The jacket could be die-cast and the liner could be removed when worn out so this construction became almost standard practice.

The high conductivity of aluminium can be used to transfer heat to a cool area. In the three-cylinder Triumph, for instance, there is no air space between the barrels, the heat being conducted through thick sections to the sides of the block. However, conductivity is not the only property required and the ability to discard heat by radiation and convection is just as important. Cast iron is better than cast aluminium in this respect but, whatever metal is used, polishing reduces the heat emission greatly. The right thing is to apply a thin coat of matt black paint as is normally done to radiator cores, even though the result will not be eye catching when exhibited outside the local pub on Saturday afternoon.

Radial fins are the "in" thing on two-strokes at present but once again are an old fashion revived; Zundaap and Villiers used radial fins long ago with good reason, because they can be made very deep without getting in each other's way, so to speak.

Beyond a certain depth parallel fins commence to act as an air blanket except at high air speeds. However impressive they may look they do not necessarily dissipate any more heat than those of more realistic proportions which is about six times the fin spacing.

8. DESMODROMIC VALVE GEAR

N obody seems to know for certain how the adjective "desmodromic" came to be applied to valve gear in which springs were replaced by some mechanical method of closing the valves. It came into use at the start of the century in connection with Peugeot racing cars and is supposed to be derived from Latin. Desmodromic can be translated loosely as "running in chains", or in other words, with a positively controlled motion, but, as the word is now an accepted part of our technical vocabulary, there is no need to pursue its derivation any further. The shortened form, "desmo", is also in common use, and one sometimes hears it applied to a Ducati as if it was a model name and not a reference to the valve gear.

Despite their universal employment to return the valves after they have been positively lifted, valve-springs have always been a target for criticism because of their liability to break, and also to limit the maximum speed of the engine through valve-bounce. These strictures were, and still are, true to a certain extent, but were originally intensified by poor spring design, inadequate material, excessively heavy valve gear and incorrect cam profiles.

As time went on and potential engine speeds rose, improvements in valve-gear design and spring technique always managed to keep the valve-gear performance abreast of the rising speeds. Today, 10.000 r.p.m. is commonplace with overhead camshafts and 5-litre 8-cylinder push rod racing engines can be taken to over 8000. Nevertheless, the possibility of spring failure and a wrecked engine is still present, while the high spring pressures required with push-rod operation load up the whole gear excessively. Mechanical return would clearly obviate much of this heavy loading and there should be virtually no limit on r.p.m. imposed by inability of the valves to follow the cams, but the problems of using "desmo" operation have been

sufficiently great to deter most people from using it or else to give it up after a while.

The very successful 1912 Peugeot car had a rudimentary form in which the twin O.H. camshafts were threaded through tappets which were shaped like stirrups, so that they were pulled back by the cams, but springs were retained on the valves.

Later attempts all made use of small springs somewhere in the system to close the valves finally, as it was thought that it would be impossible to arrange for any mechanical action to bring the valves exactly on to their seats and no further at all the varying temperatures and expansions which might exist. Either some clearance would develop and the valves would not be fully closed, or worse still, the clearance might become negative and the valves would have to stretch or break. To avoid the latter catastrophe a generous clearance can be given between the closing rocker and the valve, and a short stiff spring can be interposed to take up the varying running clearances. This idea was frequently suggested, but of course, effective operation would still depend on the reliability of the springs.

The 300 SLR Mercedes-Benz car which was once unbeatable in car racing, used such a system, employing an opening rocker and a closing rocker for

Left: External view of the Ducati cylinder head containing the dosmodromic valve-gear shown on page 47.
Below: There are no visible indications that this production Ducati employs desmodromic valve operation.

each valve, each operated by its own cam. The story goes that during a pre-race check several of these springs were found to be broken, although the engine had lost no power in practice. With little time to spare, a quick decision was made to remove all the springs so that no valve was completely closed mechanically, and the engine ran in that state for the rest of its successful life.

The explanation of this is quite simple. With any form of valve-gear, the spring or the closing rocker acts to move the valve towards the seat until it is about half-way there and is moving at maximum velocity. After that point, the momentum possessed by the valve will keep it moving without any help from the spring and it would hit the seat with a wallop except that the last portion of the cam contour is designed to slow the motion down gently and avoid heavy impact loads as the valve comes on to the seat.

If there are no closing springs and just a small amount of clearance, usually about four to six thou., there will be no compression at hand-cranking speed, but above this speed the gas cannot escape quickly enough through the very

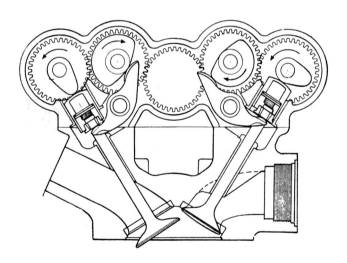

The Norton desmodromic valve gear tried experimentally in the 1959 TT practice used two shafts for each valve. The middle pair closed the valves through inverted rockers.

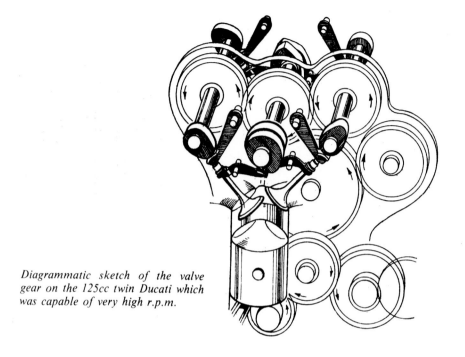

Diagrammatic sketch of the valve gear on the 125cc twin Ducati which was capable of very high r.p.m.

small seat-gaps and the valves will be blown shut and the engine will fire. At higher speeds, the operation becomes normal with the inertia of the valves making sure that they close.

Ducati introduced its desmodromic valve gear into the racing scene in 1959, using two conventional overhead camshafts and rockers to open the valves and a third centrally-mounted shaft which operated inverted fork-ended rockers for closing. One manufacturing difficulty here is to generate and time the cams so there is neither interference nor slack motion at the cross-over points where the closing cams take over from the opening ones. With no spring loading to be carried, the valve stems and rockers can be made extremely light and these Ducatis had no trouble in running to 18000 r.p.m., an unheard-of figure at that time, and more than the bottom-end would stand for very long.

Norton tried out a somewhat more complicated scheme in 1959, retaining the conventional O.H. camshafts, and followers, but including two closing camshafts driven from a central gear wheel, making a total of five gears instead of the Ducati's three. Starting this engine was quite unusual; you could push it along at a walking pace in gear as if someone had forgotten to put the plug in; but if you broke into a trot full compression came on immediately.

The Norton was not raced and the Ducatis never really shone, but I think that the full possibilities of the system were never fully exploited. My meaning is that in order to make spring-operated gear perform reliably, you are limited in cam design to contours which will not overstress the components, whereas this limitation is not so marked with desmo operation and very much higher opening and closing rates could be used.

Whatever the reasons, Ducati is the only firm to persevere with it, the latest version being fitted to the Super Sports twins which have done well in endurance production races. In this design, each head carries a central shaft with two opening and two closing cams, each operating the appropriate rockers and making a very neat and compact assembly. Each closing rocker has a hairpin type valve-spring which takes up the small valve clearance at low speeds and is said to promote good starting and idling, but breakage of these springs would not affect the power output. Clearance adjustment is not a particularly easy matter as it is made by using valve stem caps and collars of varying thickness, but once set, the clearances should remain constant for a long time.

Four rockers and one camshaft are utilised to operate the desmodromic valve gear of the 850cc V-twin Ducati. Light springs are included to ensure closing at low speeds.

48

9. SIDE-VALVES

At a period when makers of four-stroke engines appear to be engaged in a competition as to which one can design the most complicated machinery, it may seem a trifle odd to advance any arguments in favour of the side-valve engine which for three or four decades was standard equipment in the majority of motorized vehicles of all types.

With the advent of efficient push-rod engines and improved manufacturing technique, the side-valve gradually fell out of favour until nowadays it is practically confined to small industrial engines where cheapness is the main consideration and buyers do not care what sort of valves are installed.

This is not to say that cheapness and simplicity are the side-whacker's only virtues. In its heyday, some examples worked extremely well by the standards then prevailing, turning out performances equal to, or even better than rival O.H.V. models, and on the whole were more reliable.

The mechanical mayhem which inevitably followed an all-too-frequent overhead valve breakage before austenitic exhaust valve steels were developed did not plague the side-valve to nearly the same extent. If a valve head did come off, it usually stayed harmlessly in the pocket instead of wrecking the piston and the valves never hit each other if a gear-change was missed.

At this juncture, the thought occurs to me that some first-generation riders, brought up either on two-strokes or overhead-camshaft fourstrokes might not even know how a sidevalve engine is constructed, so a brief explanation might be in order for their benefit. Vintage types can skip the next few lines.

In its earliest form, the valves, usually of identical size and material, ran

49

in guides at one side and parallel to the cylinder, which had an integral head with two screwed caps to enable the valves to be installed. The combustion chamber was flat and of almost constant height above the valves and cylinder (as shown in the diagram) and the ports were frequently of poor shape with square corners and sharp changes in the direction of gas flow. Such designs were fundamentally poor performers, partly because their breathing ability was bad, and partly because they knocked or detonated very badly unless the compression ratio was only 4 to 1 or thereabouts.

Cylinder distortion due to unequal cooling of the area adjacent to the exhaust port was also a problem, causing the power to fall off on long hills, a malady colloquially referred to as "drying-up". J. L. Norton was probably the first man to appreciate the severity of this effect and iminimized it by constructing the famous 490cc long-stroke model with an air-space between the cylinder and exhaust port, the latter being smoothly contoured.

Back in 1911, D. R. O'Donovan established many records with this engine in "Old Miracle", his best short-distance effort being one mile at 82.5 m.p.h. (132.8km.h) — on 70 octane fuel! In passing, this machine still

One of the most highly developed side-valves the 45 cub-in Indian seen here in hill-climb trim.

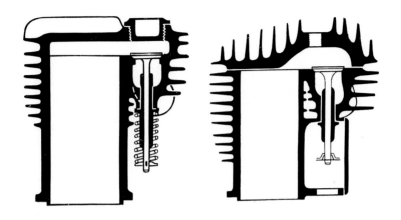

Above: The early fixed-head cylinder (a) was detonation proned and poorly cooled. A much better combustion space and greater turbulance is provided by the Ricardo-type detachable head (b).

exists, and I have had the pleasure of riding it in the grounds of the Montague Motor Museum. It would throttle down to a walking pace on its single 3½ to 1 gear and was still capable of over 75m.p.h.

The next big step forward was the invention of the Ricardo head, in which most of the combustion chamber was located over the valves — the remainder of the head being flat and only just clearing the piston crown. The effect was to squish a quantity of mixture violently into the valve pocket near t.d.c., creating an internal turbulence which speeded up the combustion process. Also the mixture trapped in the squish area remote from the sparking plug was cooled so effectively that compression ratios up to 8 to 1 could be used without detonation. Less ignition advance was required and the engine was far less dependent on the manual ignition control which was an essential adjunct to the earlier engines.

Enclosed valves and off-set exhaust ports on the 1200cc Indian "Super-Chief".

The Ricardo head was patented and users had to pay a royalty which though small, was unwelcome and not everyone adopted the principle. For instance, the very early A.J.S. engine had a detachable head which included the valve pocket and ports, thereby considerably reducing distortion of the cylinder. This construction was retained, but some degree of squish was provided by adding a raised crown to the piston.

A properly tuned 350 side-valve A.J.S., running on alcohol could do close to 80m.p.h. (130km.h) in the middle 20's and was one of the easiest engines to work on ever built. It is no exaggeration to say that you could have the head, barrel and piston sitting on the bench in less than five minutes after stopping the engine.

The advent of the Ricardo head led to the use of detachable well-finned aluminium heads without the valve caps which were prone to overheat unless they were of the "fir-cone" variety introduced on J.A.P. engines, for the fixed-head models which for their time were very fast. From the mechanical aspect, the valve gear is almost as light and free from flexure as overhead camshaft gear, so the attainable revs are limited more by breathing than by valve-float. The 250cc J.A.P. built in 1921 was reputed to rev to 8000r.p.m. and it could give any push-rod engine a good run for its money, especially in hill climbs. However, the side-whacker gradually fell out of favour as push-rod and O.H.C. engines became more powerful and more reliable. It was mainly retained in England in slow-speed woolly engines intended chiefly for sidecar work, although the 8-45 J.A.P. 1000cc twin was used extensively on big fast models like the Brough-Superior and Coventry-Eagle.

The position was somewhat different in America, where the side-valve

The 1920 250cc JAP with "fir-cone" valve caps was very fast for its time. The vertical pipe between the valves sprayed oil onto the valve stems through small holes.

Below: The iron cylinder and the aluminium head of the KRTT Harley Davidson. Note the large inlet valves and the off-set exhaust port.

replaced the traditional inlet-over-exhaust arrangement on Harleys and Indians. The 45 cubic inch Harley twin designed over forty years ago and used for touring and military models was later developed for racing under A.M.A. rules into a very formidable device, capable of propelling the KRTT model at around 140m.p.h. (225km.h), when running on alcohol-blend fuel. This was despite the rather peculiar inlet port shape necessitated partly by the use of a single carburettor mounted on a T-shaped manifold, so that the incoming charge has to turn twice through 90 degrees before entering the cylinder.

Urge reputed to exceed 55b.h.p. at around 7000r.p.m. was obtained with very radical valve timing, the inlet opening 66 degrees before t.d.c. and closing at 82 degrees measured at .010 lift, but the bottom fell out of the power curve below 4500 r.p.m. This would be easily the most well-developed sidevalve ever made and it could have been still further improved by using two carburettors with much straighter ports, but the A.M.A. racing regulations did not permit this.

One difficulty with side valves is the problem of obtaining a high compression ration without restricting the breathing space inside the head. It is difficult to exceed 9 to 1 without loss of power at high revs, and the Harley is said to be even lower partly because the valves are of relatively enormous dimensions.

In the car world side-valve engines, besides being very durable, were also used extensively for racing Austin 7's won a 500 mile race at Brooklands and also won the first Australian G.P. run at Phillip Island in Victoria in 1928. At the other end of the scale, a 1929 model Austin 7 was recently driven round the world covering 64,000 miles (103,000km) in the process, with no engine trouble except the occasional valve-grind, which the owner did himself in an hour or two. Similarly the flat-head Ford V8 won countless races, while a ten year old model won the first Round-Australia Redex Trial in 1954.

So you see that despite its virtual disappearance, there is quite a lot to be said in the side-valve's favour. It can be smaller, lighter, and easier to make or assemble than an O.H.V. of the same capacity and will provide good acceleration and excellent fuel consumption. It will fall short in sheer power, but this is probably the least important factor of all where average riding is concerned, despite the current worship of high power whatever penalties of inflexibility, heavy fuel consumption and excessive complexity are incurred.

10. SUPERCHARGING

To the uninitiated, the subject of supercharging has a faint air of black magic about it and the fact that it is banned for road-racing adds a sort of "forbidden fruit" flavour, accentuated by its permitted and frequent use on the fire-breathing monsters used in drag-racing.

Turbocharging even manages to sound a trifle mysterious, but in a way the title is misleading, as it only implies that the supercharger is driven by an exhaust-driven turbine and not by the engine directly.

The word supercharging means raising the pressure of the air at the entrance to the cylinder above that of the surrounding atmosphere so that the engine can inhale more than it could by its own unaided efforts. Just how this object is achieved is quite immaterial; you could use a cylinder of compressed air or even a pair of blacksmith's bellows, but the conventional system is to employ a blower either of the Roots, or the eccentric vane types, chain or belt-driven from the mainshaft at the speed necessary to give something around 10 to 20 pounds pressure above atmospheric, according to the sort of performance you need, and how much the engine will stand. I should point out that I've no inclination to state pressures in kilopascals as this would be meaningless to many readers. In broad terms power output is proportional to the absolute pressure, that is to say, the pressure above absolute zero.

Normal atmospheric pressure is 14.7 pounds absolute, which can be taken as 15 for all practical purposes. A supercharger gauge pressure of 15 pounds is equal to 30 pounds absolute, so that at this pressure the engine should give double its normal power. In practice it will not do so for various reasons, especially if the engine was originally a high-compression unit with long valve timing and a lot of overlap.

The blower itself will absorb several horse-power, thus reducing the net

55

output, but in order to cope with the heavier weight of mixture shoved down its throat, the engine's compression ration will need to be lowered from, say 12 to 1 to around 9 to 1, otherwise it will knock itself to death or melt the piston crown.

During the overlap period when both valves are open, some of the mixture which has taken some energy to compress, will go straight out through the exhaust valve. In order to reduce this loss, the overlap must be reduced from around 120 degrees to about 40 degrees. So, in the finish, the power you will supposedly be doubling is not that of a racing engine, but only that of a good sports engine. On the other hand, the engine would be much more flexible and have about 50 percent more torque in the middle range, so it would be a better proposition for all-round work, except for the added weight.

Supercharging had quite a vogue for road-racing machines in the 1930-39 period, the most successful four-strokes being the Guzzi and later the BMW. However, the trend was viewed with disfavour because it was rightly considered to be an easy method of sidestepping the capacity regulations, and the F.I.M. decided in 1946 to ban supercharging for all competitions except record-breaking and sprint events. This decision put a spoke in the wheel of the A.J.S. "Porcupine" which was originally designed especially for supercharging and although it won a World Championship it never really recovered from being converted to atmospheric. The ban also had a marked

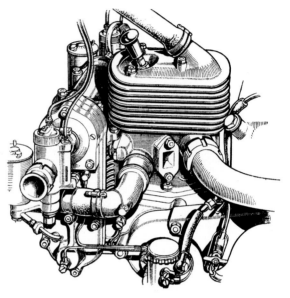

affect on the development of the two-stroke because even methods of increasing the crankcase pumping ability by using double-diameter pistons or extra charging pistons were excluded, and thus forced D.K.W. to abandon the very successful, but very complicated and fuel-consuming two strokes on which several of these schemes had been employed. This firm, which was committed to the two-stroke, had to seek other methods and as a result evolved the 3-cylinder 350 c.c. machine which was probably the first example of the use of expansion chambers on a racing machine.

Where record-breaking is concerned and alcohol fuel is allowed, the position is somewhat different. The extra weight does not matter much nor does the fuel consumption, while the internal cooling effect and knock-resistance of methanol permits a high compression ratio to be retained. Consequently, for fifty years the World Record has mostly been held by supercharged machines, although the Vincent which held it in 1955 at 185 m.p.h. was atmospheric.

With turbo-charging, the compressor is of the centrifugal type, with the runner mounted on the same shaft as the impellor of a turbine driven by the exhaust from the engine. Both components are only a few centimetres in

diameter and the combined unit is small enough to be mounted on the outlet end of the exhaust manifold. The turbine runs at colossal r.p.m., maybe 150,000 or more when the engine is on full song, and as the power is derived from the speed of the exhaust gas, you get it for nothing, so to speak, and the obstruction to gas-flow is so small that not much back pressure is created. The trouble is that throttle-response is very poor, for two reasons. If the throttle is opened at low speed there is not enough exhaust gas to make the turbine speed rise immediately, but thereafter, if the throttle is held steady the turbine speed and the blower pressure will both rise at a rapidly increasing rate, until either the engine blows up or the rear wheels spin — or

both. To avoid this it is necessary to include a waste-gate which is merely a valve that opens and allows some of the exhaust gas to escape before it reaches the turbine.

Turbochargers work well on big Deisel engines running mainly at a governed speed, and also on racing cars performing at Indianapolis, where the circuit consists of four straights and four bends with an engine speed range of 6500 - 8500 r.p.m. The 2.6 litre 4-cylinder Offenhauser used on this circuit is said to develop 600 b.h.p. but would not be of much use on a course where a lot of gear changing was required.

A friend of mine who turbo-charged a Holden touring car found that in ordinary driving and particularly in traffic, it was little, if any quicker after conversion than before, and although it was faster on long straights, it was liable to become feverish if the speed was maintained. I fear that his findings will be duplicated by anyone who decides to fit a turbo-charger to a road going motorcycle, and uses the machine on roads where its full potential can be realized.

The 1938 BMW was designed very neatly, with the supercharger and carburettor mounted in front of the engine. The complete machine weighed only 304 lbs.

11. WHEELS

T he wheel was invented so long ago that nobody really knows where the idea originated. Over the centuries, the original disc form, probably made by cutting a slice from a hollow log, was eventually replaced by built-up wheels with wooden hubs, spokes and rims held together by metal tyres. This basic design remained almost unchanged for centuries except in detail, and is still in use but is essentially only suitable for low speeds on smooth or soft surfaces.

The earliest two-wheeled machines such as the "hobby-horse" and the velocipede, propelled by foot power, used this form of wheel, but it was too heavy and too bone-shattering on cobbled roads to be tolerated except by a few eccentric riders. It was soon replaced by the wire wheel, with a light rolled-steel or wooden rim connected to a flanged hub with steel spokes, a much lighter construction which also possessed a small amount of flexibility and gave a smoother ride on that account.

At first, the spokes were disposed radially when viewed from the side, but this method was soon dropped in favour of the tangential system, in which the spokes are much better able to cope with power or braking torque applied to the hub. In this method of lacing, the spokes on either side are in two sets, one being approximately tangential to the hub flange and angled forwards, the other also being tangential but angled backwards, each spoke of one set crossing those in the other set twice or thrice before reaching the rim. As the spokes are not radial to the rim and also all slope inwards at angles determined by the width and diameter of the hub flanges, the rim has to be specially punched or drilled at a compound angle so that the threaded nipples can seat squarely without creating local kinks in the spokes. Ideally, the hub flanges should be of equal diameter and distance from the centre because the spokes will then be all of the same length and the rim will also be

symmetrical, but this is not always the case so that unsymmetrical punching becomes necessary. There are so many different hub disigns and rim sizes in existance that it is impossible for a repair shop to stock rims ready to fit except in a few popular sizes, and it is necessary to get the rims specially drilled to suit individual applications.

The fundamental difference between a solid-spoked wheel and a wire wheel is that in the former the axle load places the lower spokes in compression in which direction they are very rigid, but in the wire wheel the lowest spokes cannot carry any load, and it is all in effect suspended from the top of the rim by the upper spokes which being thin can stretch elastically by a small amount under tension.

When loaded in this way, the rim tends to distort into an oval shape, but is prevented from doing so by the horizontal spokes. In fact all the spokes do their share in maintaining circularity, the stress steadily increasing from zero in the lower spokes to a maximum in the upper ones. In addition to the live load there is, of course, the tension applied to all the spokes when the wheel is built and trued up. By rights, this should be equal all the way round, but if the rim is buckled or out of round, attempting to get it to run true by over-tightening some spokes is very likely to result in them rapidly failing in service. Usually one spoke breaks first, throwing more load on the others, which fail one after the other until the wheel collapses. This sequence may occur under tough conditions even with a well-built wheel, and it is imperative when travelling in very rough country to carry spare spokes to enable replacements to be made on the spot, as it is highly unlikely that spares of the correct type will be available, except from main agents — and sometimes not even then.

62

Left: Solid spoked wheels on the 1885 Daimler — the world's first petrol driven motorcycle.

The spokes of the 500cc Moto Guzzi racer front wheel were all of equal length and equal angles.

Spokes are made with a cold-forged head, and usually, though not always, are sharply bent close to the head to form a hook engaging with the flange. This form of attachment, though simple, tends to overstress the metal adjacent to the bend, with consequent liability to failure, expecially if the wire is of the same gauge for its whole length. To avoid this, the best quality spokes are butted, that is to say, a short length at the head end is two gauges heavier than the rest, which greatly increases the strength without increasing the weight much or reducing the elasticity.

The outer ends are usually formed by rolling the thread rather than cutting it, as less local weakening is caused. A rolled thread can easily be recognized because it is a little larger than the wire diameter, the difference being more easily detected by "feel" rather than by sight. Nipples to suit cut threads will not screw on to rolled threads, but while rolled-thread nipples will screw on to cut threads, the fit is so poor that the threads are certain to strip when loaded. Generally speaking, a cut-thread spoke should never be used except as a last

Cast wheels, pioneered for racing by Peter Williams, have since become popular for road work. The Italian Laverda factory is fortunate enough to have its own foundry and manufacturers its own wheels. The pic. left is of the Laverda 1000 front wheel.

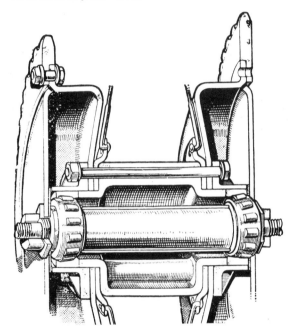

Part section of the 1934 Vincent HRD duo-brake hub showing the spokes of equal length attached to flanges separate from the drums. Two sprockets can be carried for rapid changes of gear ratio. The Series B brakes are similar but the detailed construction is different.

resort if a repair has to be made far from home, and it should be replaced at the first opportunity. Some spokes are fairly easy to change, especially if the flange has key-hole slots instead of plain holes, but others can be very awkward. It is worth checking this point before buying a bush-bashing bicycle.

Spokes should always be examined after a spell of rough riding, or even after an isolated incident such as running over a kerb. Any loose ones should be re-tightened, otherwise they are not carrying their share of the load and the adjacent ones may break. If the rim is buckled, some attempt can be made to get it running true by varying the spoke tensions but trying for perfection at the expense of overtightening some spokes is not a good idea. It is better to settle for a little wobble in the rim and unequally-tensioned spokes until a chance arrives to rebuild the wheel. The flats formed on the nipples for tightening them distort very easily, so a properly fitting key should form part of every rough-riders' tool kit.

In the best wheels, all the spokes are of equal length and gauge and lie at equal angles. They then share all loads equally and also all have the same degree of elasticity. This situation can be found when the brake drum, disc or sprocket is bolted to the hub directly, and was also a feature of the many quickly-detachable wheels which manufacturers once rightly considered to be essential on a touring machine.

When one spoke-flange is formed on a drum which itself is integral with the hub, the spokes on that side are shorter than those on the other side and also lie at a greater cone angle. They are therefore subjected to greater stress, but have less elasticity and invariably this side is prone to spoke breakage. Fitting heavier spokes on that side only is not necessarily a cure because they have even less elasticity than before, but using a larger gauge on the other side also will probably improve the situation. One merit of the so-called full-width brake drum with two large flanges, is that the spokes are symmetrically disposed, but on the other hand, unequal spoke tensions can pull the drum out of round and adversely affect an otherwise excellent brake.

A few wheels with solid spokes have been used from time to time, but were never appreciated until Peter Williams of Norton Villiers started racing successfully with cast magnesium-alloy wheels of his own design. Since then they have become the "in" thing in racing equipment and a number of slightly differing designs have appeared, the difference being mainly in the number or angular location of the spokes. Some are said to show a considerable saving in weight, but Peter Williams told me that his own were not much lighter than wire wheels, their main advantage being that the brake calipers could be mounted closer in.

Collapse of a wheel by rim breakage between the spokes is fraught with such peril that it is better to err on the safe side and not to skimp the material in an effort to make a very light component lighter still. There is also another matter to consider. Magnesium alloys have a destressing habit of developing cracks which gradually extend with time until something breaks. For this reason, racing car wheels have to be rejected after a three-year life, but of course, they are subjected to very high lateral cornering forces which are not applied to the wheels on a solo bike. Fortunately, aluminium wheels do not suffer from this defect and have a longer expected life, but the rims are more likely to be severely damaged by rocks than the more resilient steel variety.

12. WHEEL BALANCING

W hile competition men are fully aware of the necessity to balance their road wheels accurately, it is not always appreciated that a lack of balance, especially at the front, can give rise to some undesirable effect even at quite moderate speeds.

One is a kind of muted vibration of the front wheel, which becomes more pronounced as a particular speed is approached, and then dies away at higher speed. This is due to the vertical component of the centrifugal force generated by the imbalance coming into resonance with the bouncing frequency of the tyre on the road, or of the whole unsprung mass acting against the fork springs, and is more unpleasant than it is dangerous except perhaps when rounding a corner at the critical speed.

In other cases, the effect may become steadily more pronounced as the speed rises, and it is even possible for the tyre tread to be lifted clear of the ground once per revolution, which is clearly not good at all.

The long-term result of running an unbalanced wheel is to wear the tread rubber unevenly, thereby making the imbalance worse instead of better, and on all counts, it pays to check periodically and if necessary, to correct the wheel balance on a fast machine, especially if long journeys on sealed roads are to be undertaken.

Lack of balance can be caused by all sorts of factors. The valve constitutes a heavy spot, the tyre itself may be heavier on one side than the other, security bolts may have been added or the rim and tyre may be out of round. The essence of the thing is that the centre of gravity of the wheel, including the brake drum or disc must be exactly on the axis of the hub, and even if the rim and tyre appear to be truly circular, the wheel will still be out of balance

Right: The usual method of balancing is to wrap lead stands around the spokes and finally secure it with tape.

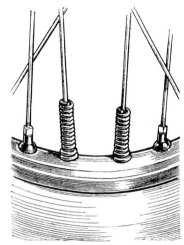

Below: the two variable balance weights fitted as trandard on the Vicnent HRD front wheel can be clearly seen in the picture of the prototype model built in 1946.

HRD

GNK564

if they are eccentric, even by an amount so small as to be almost unnoticeable. Correction is performed by adding weight to the light side, but how this is done is of no importance, except that a small amount placed on or near the rim will be as effective as a heavier weight located at a smaller radius. If desired, more than one weight can be used and placed at different angles around the rim as for instance, on the Vincent wheels which were supplied as standard with two built-in variable balance weights, each located one-third of the way round from the valve.

The usual method of verifying the balance is by supporting the forks with the tyre clear of the ground and in bad cases, the wheel will oscillate back and forth for a few times and finally come to rest with the heavy spot at the bottom. If the imbalance is not very severe, little or no oscillation will occur but can be stimulated by tapping the axle lightly with a hammer or a lump of wood. The heavy spot can be fairly accurately assessed by averaging the results of several checks, marking the lowest point of the tyre each time with chalk or sticky tape, but the results will be very inconsistent if there is any friction present to prevent free movement. This usually arises from the brakes which sometimes bind even when slackened right off, but even if there is no drag from this source,there may still be enough resistance set up by stiff hub-seals to make accurate observations difficult, and it may be necessary to remove them for the time being. Bearings which are badly adjusted or even packed with heavy grease will have the same effect, and a real stickler for perfection will even dismantle the hub and reassemble it correctly, using only thin oil as a temporary lubricant. There is nothing wrong with this policy as long as he remembers to repack the bearings afterwards.

Having determined the heavy side after all this preliminary work, the next step with wire wheels is to place the wheel with the heavy side level with the axle and wind some lead wire or strip around the spokes near the rim on the opposite side, increasing the amount until the wheel shows no tendency for the marked line to rise or fall. However, it is quite likely that this mark was not exactly in the correct plane, which will be shown up by turning it to the topmost position. If the wheel then shows a tendency to rotate in one direction, weight can be added at right angles to the mark until this tendency is removed, or alternatively, the first weight can be moved a little way round the rim in the required direction. You may have to go over the whole process several times before finality is reached, because the nearer the balance approaches perfection, the harder it becomes to detect and eliminate the progressively smaller errors.

While lead wire is a commonly used material, it is a bit too soft to be able to retain itself safely, so it must be tightly bound with adhesive tape, which not being entirely weightless, must be allowed for in the last stages of balancing.

If security bolts located some distance apart are fitted, they can be used as balance weights by adding washers to them, while for solid or cast magnesium wheels with only a few spokes, the self-adhesive lead strip available from "speed-shops" is very handy. It must, however, be placed inside the rim so that centrigual force will tend to hold it in place instead of tearing it off.

Obviously, it is a waste of time to do all this work unless the wheel and tyre are in good condition, because any subsequent wheel-truing or tyre-changing will almost certainly destroy the balance. In fact, if the tyre is taken off and put back in a different position you may be worse off than before balancing was performed.

It sometimes happens that on a country journey a wheel becomes damaged or bent to an extent which cannot be fully rectified under the circumstances, but the imbalance may be bad enough to make riding uncomfortable or risky. In such an event, even a rough balancing job will be better than nothing, even if it entails pinching some wire out of a fence or taping some nuts or small bots to the spokes. Lack of balance shows up much more at the front than at the rear, but nevertheless, it is a good idea to balance both wheels if the model is capable of very high speeds, or if the rear suspension is very soft and has a long travel as on scramble machines where the knobby rear tyre constitutes a considerable proportion of the total machine weight. Even if the wheel is balanced, a lump of mud and grass stuck inside the rim or even a rimful of mud from which a piece has fallen out, can create intense vibration, as can be discovered by running the engine in top gear with the model raised on the centre stand. A badly unbalanced wheel can "chop" very badly under wheel-spinning conditions in soft soil as it is alternately forced into contact or lifted away from the surface.

The very wide rims and tyres now being fitted to racing sidecar outfits can suffer from another form of imbalance caused by the tyre being heavier at one side than it is on the same side but diametrically opposite, the kind of effect you would get by applying a heavy patch to the side-wall. This sort of condition will cause the front wheel to oscillate from side to side at wheel speed, and cannot be cured by the static method previously described. It can only be done by means of apparatus designed for balancing car wheels while they are attached to their own hubs, or with one of the several machines designed for "off-the-car" balancing. Any of these will perform both static and dynamic balancing very quickly and accurately but are only suitable for bolt-on detachable wheels and not for the normal motorcycle variety.

13. SOME HISTORIC INDIANS

One generally notable omission when enthusiasts talk of historic Indian motorcycles is the "Light Twin" which was a radical departure from the big V-twins which had already established a good reputation by the time that the Light Twin came out in 1917.

It had a 250cc side-valve flat-twin engine with the cylinders lying for-and aft, magneto ignition and an outside flywheel.

According to the descriptive brochure, the cylinders were provided with "generous cooling fins", but as these were at right-angles to the air-flow and the rear cylinder was badly shrouded, it is doubtful if the claimed output of the "full brake horse power" could have been sustained for any appreciable distance. The brochure also claimed the machine provided "shockless, joltless, noiseless, jerkless riding comfort" but in view of the rigid forks this statement was probably just a wee-bit exaggerated and in any case these attributes were not sufficient to keep the model in production for long. Wal Maynard of the Vintage MCC of Victoria has restored one to what he trusts is its pristine vigor.

The 350cc single-cylinder Indian "Prince" was brought out in 1925 as a counterblast to the small English machines, which were beginning to gain a foothold in the American market. It was a more successful model than the "Light Twin" and was evidently the outcome of a close study of several imported machines. It had a rigid frame and girder forks with a central spring and except for the colour scheme, bore a strong resemblance to the Raleigh. The engine had a detachable cylinder head and one of the gems in the publicity material which caused some amusement was the statement that the head could be removed and replaced 72 times without renewing the gasket. Nobody seemed to know why such a monumental number of detachments

Above: The 596cc V-twin "Scout" was probably the most popular Indian ever made. This is a well preserved example.

Left: The performance of this neatly designed 433cc twin was not good enough to please traditional Indian riders.

would ever be required but some prospective customers seemed to be impressed. The Prince was not very fast, but it was reliable and the Australian rider Vic Barclay broke a couple of intercapital records on one.

The 216cc single and 433 parallel twin which were introduced after the War were reputedly designed for the Indian factory by two Dutchmen named Stockvis. They had been virtually hounded out of their business as DKW distributors in Holland by the Nazi regime on account of their Jewish blood. Being also Velocette agents they came over to Birmingham with a 125 DKW to see if Velocette could produce a similar model. I was at Velocette at the time and after the machine was completely dismantled, we concluded that we had no machine tools suitable for the job. They then went to Tony Wilson-Jones of Royal Enfield, who agreed to the project and production started in time to supply a large number to the air-borne troops for use against the German army. Rather a nice twist of fate.

Later on the Stockvis brothers went to the States and there became involved in the new Indians which were a costly failure partly because of their low performance and the fact that they were too lightly built to be reliable. And also partly because to buyers loyal to the name-plate, an Indian just had to look like an Indian, which at the period meant a cumbersome but impressive "V" twin. This venture was said to have cost several million dollars for tooling-up and the factory was disinclined to repeat the process with another design despite the falling sales of the 74 cubic inch Super Chief, which was then the factory's only answer to the

The "Light Twin" model O Indian restored by its owner Wal Maynard of the Vintage M.C.C. Melbourne.

Harley Davidson. The Vincent was also beginning to penetrate the market following its capture of the American speed record.

In 1948 when P. C. Vincent was conducting a sales campaign in North America, he met a very suave gentleman who happened to be the head man in the Indian company which was by then in very low water. An English businessman named Brockhouse, who owned a number of engineering companies, was anxious to obtain a controlling interest in Indian, and the upshot of discussions by the three was that if the Vincent unit could be fitted in the Super Chief frame without much alteration, the result would be a very saleable machine with financial benefit to all concerned.

On receipt of drawings in England, I made a quick check which confirmed the feasibility of the scheme and the result was that the Indian company would contract to buy 100 power units and 50 Vincents with American electrical equipment per week, provided Brockhouse could get a permit from the British Government to export the funds necessary to buy a controlling interest in Indian. This was very probable in view of the value of the orders mentioned. There would also need to be some finance injected into the Vincent Company to cover the greatly increased purchases of material but this was dismissed as a mere matter of a signature on a cheque.

Everything worked pretty quickly. A Super Chief was shot over to Stevenage and as a preliminary it was road tested. Its 580 pounds weight seemed enormous compared to the 450 pound Rapide and while it could attain 88 m.p.h. for a short distance, the sustained maximum was only about 80.

After removing the engine and sawing off some unwanted frame parts, the Vincent unit fitted in like a kernel in a nut. Engine plates were used instead of the standard cylinder head brackets and the existing foot boards and brake pedal were retained but some cross-over linkage had to be devised in

Below: The four cylinder model, made around 1940, was a descendant of the Indian-Ace and had the same cooling problems.

order to use the near side heel-and-toe clutch pedal as a gear change pedal. The dynamo remained in the original position under the saddle (sorry . . . buddy-seat), and was belt-driven from a short shaft and pulley in the space normally occupied by our Miller generator. The accompanying photo shows how snugly the unit fitted in and also the way in which separate exhaust pipes were used in order to retain the existing silencers.

The conversion job took only a couple of weeks and although the finished article was not much lighter than the original, the performance was vastly improved. Top speed went to 104 and it was as fast in second gear as it used to be in top. Changing gear by foot instead of by hand improved acceleration. Fuel consumption, although not as good as with the Rapide, improved from about 35 m.p.g. to more like 50.

A Rapide was fitted with American electrics and the rear brake and gear pedals changed over and the two machines were presented to the Board of Trade. Brockhouse received permission to export the funds required to buy the Indian Co. as the proposed arrangement would have brought several million dollars per year back into England.

Below: End of a long line of Indians from Springfield Mass., the 1200cc Super Chief.

To cope with the increased output, orders for castings, forgings and accessories, had been doubled and material was beginning to come in. So were the bills, but the money so glibly promised, failed to materialize on the flimsy and quite untrue grounds that the plant and stock did not provide sufficient asset backing. Vincent had thus been wangled into an intolerable position with the possibility of an enforced liquidation and sale of the factory to the highest bidder, and there are no prizes for guessing just who that would have been. However, this situation was averted by action of the official receiver after which the whole scheme fell to the ground. This was a great pity because if it had come off, there is little doubt that the Indian would have remained on the market and the Vincent factory also would have benefitted financially. As it was, the Indian Co. was forced to sell an insignificant 250cc model to keep going at all and afterwards handled Royal Enfield bearing the Indian transfer. Finally the company was acquired by Associated Motor Cycles in 1953 and the history of the famous company founded by George Hendee, came to an end.

14. TWO RARE VELOCETTES

T he arrival and success of supercharged multi-cylinder racing machines in the late 1930's seemed to indicate clearly that the "atmospheric" single cylinder had had its day. But bearing in mind that Velocette policy was always to market a model bearing at least a family resemblance to the racers what was to take the place of the TT single?

In Hall Green's estimation the flat twin was too wide and vulnerable and possessed undesirable torque reactions, the parallel twin vibrated badly and four cylinders appeared to be two too many. Conversely a parallel twin with fore-and-aft crankshafts geared together to run in opposite directions would be compact, reasonably simple and would be free from inertia torque reactions. It would also provide a straightline drive to an engine-speed gear box with enough offset for a propeller shaft to clear the tyre on its way to a final drive bevel box, while the idle crankshaft could drive a supercharger directly on the racer and accept the generator and kick start mechanism on the tourer.

With the basic layout agreed upon, Charles Udall was given the task of designing the racer, later on to be nick-named the "Roarer", from its rather flat exhaust note. The tourer was allocated to me and given the type letter "O" as being the next in suitable alphabetical order after the "M" range.

At all times the three technical directors of Velcoe Ltd. Percy and Eugene Goodman and Harold Willis collaborated in the designs and the service manager, Bob Burgess, often had a few comments to make on points which would affect his department in the future.

On the "O" it was desirable to utilise as many existing components as possible. One way was to mount the gear box on the right hand side as this would bring the foot change mechanism in a convenient position and it was not very difficult to modify the MOV gear box shafts to enable power to go in at the front and out at the rear. The ratios chosen were 1, 1.2, 1.75 and 2.55 to 1.

Instead of going through the box, the kick starter (fully folding) was mounted on the frame and drove via a small bevel box to the left hand crankshaft through a quickly detachable coupling. This arrangement

The author astride the model 'O' Velocette during many thousands of test miles in England.

permitted starts to be made in gear with the clutch out, a method which has lately become very fashionable.

For some reason Udall preferred to mount his supercharger (also made by Veloce) on the right and put a very special gear box on the left. Consequently his crankshafts turned outwards and mine turned inwards. His coupling gears were at the rear which was actually a better place than at the front where mine were put for ease of assembly and other minor reasons.

At this juncture it may be less confusing to leave the Roarer and concentrate upon the other features of the "O" where it was necessary to keep manufacturing costs as low as possible as it was obviously a more expensive proposition than a chain driven single cylinder like the MSS. To this end, the engine mainshafts and crankpins were ground parallel and press fitted into "T" shaped webs without keys or nuts. Chrome plated sleeves were provided on the crank pins upon which forged RR56 aluminium alloy solid-eye connecting rods ran directly. The small ends were also unbushed but enough metal was provided to allow for boring and bushing if ever the need arose.

The main bearings were renewable bushes lined with light metal. Full pressure lubrication was provided from a gear pump in the sump carrying oil to all bearings and also to a jet impinging on the coupling gears at the point where the teeth came out of mesh which seems wrong but is actually the correct method as shown by laboratory tests.

By sheer coincidence the coupling gears were of almost identical size and tooth pitch to those in the Ariel Square Four but whereas the latter were of hardened steel with fibre discs rivetted on to suppress ringing I elected to try high-tensile cast iron which would be less expensive and probably less noisy. These gears and a thin seven-inch steel flywheel on the left shaft were enclosed in the front cover and external pipes were absent except for one leading to the rocker gear.

The cast iron cylinder block contained both barrels spaced sufficiently wide apart to provide an airflow between them and also to accommodate the pushrods. These were actuated by followers sliding in a cast iron tappet block and a short camshaft driven by an eight millimetre pitch duplex chain from the left crankshaft.

The final engine dimensions were intended to be 68.2mm stroke and 68mm bore so that MOV pistons could be used, but for test purposes the bores were increased to 74mm to take KSS pistons the capacity being thereby increased from 498 to 588cc.

The aluminium cylinder head was also a one-piece casting. Following normal Velo practice, it had inserted valve seats and bronze guides and the rockers which oscillated on hardened steel shafts were shaped so that the screwed adjusters all lay in a small square in the centre where they were easy to get at after removal of the large two-bolt cover enclosing the whole valve gear. All very simple and dead easy to overhaul.

The *final* shaft drive and the adjustable rear springing are features of interest on the Model 'O' (opposite).

The supercharger of the Velocette "Roarer" can just be seen low down behind the crankcase. Note the rearward facing exhaust ports.

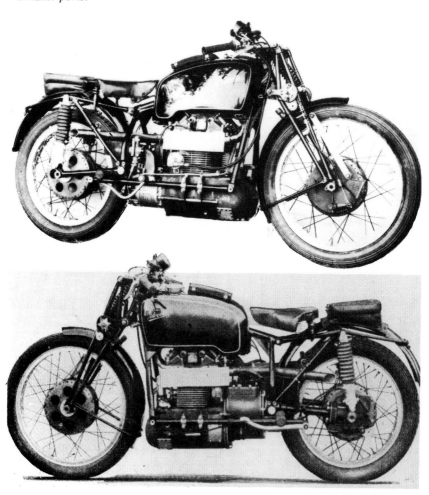

The coil ignition distributor was driven directly from the rear of the camshaft, both it and the generator being concealed beneath a sheet metal cover which also hid the starting mechanism and extended over the gear box to provide an easily cleaned exterior.

Whereas the propeller shaft on the Roarer was enclosed in the left hand fork tube, on the "O" it was open at this simplified removal of the final drive when a change of gear ratio was desired.

Two sets of bevel gears were made with ratios 9:43 and 8:45, the resulting overall ratios being 4.8, 5.82, 8.43 and 12.3 for solo use and 5.62,: 6.8,: 9.7 and 14.3 to 1 for sidecar work.

With the aid of a roll-on centre stand, a hinged rear guard and just one spanner, the rear wheel could be removed in about a minute leaving the brake shoes attached to the bevel box with the adjustment unaltered.

For experimental purposes the front end all consisted of standard MSS components but the main frame had widely spaced duplex tubes running down to and back alongside the unit and then up to the saddle lug.

Although a geared twin has perfect primary balance a high-frequency secondary vibration exists and to combat any tremor which might arise, the engine was mounted on two rubber-bushed brackets at the front and one on a cross member at the rear. The entire unit could be lifted into the frame very quickly leaving only the usual pipes and wires to be connected.

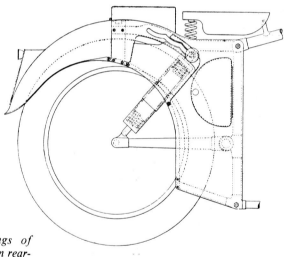

Patent drawings of the stressed skin rear-end and adjustable suspension embodied in the Model '0' and post-war Velocettes. This foreshadowed the modern trend towards "laid-down" shock absorbers.

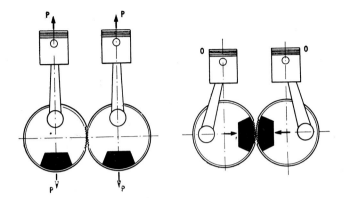

How 100 per cent counterweighting gives perfect primary balance with contra-rotating cranks.

Although only of the untriangulated type, the swinging rear fork had a very massive transverse lug adjacent to the pivot bearings in order to resist the torque reactions of considerable magnitude which arise with shaft drive under power or braking, tending to twist the rear wheel out of line unless the fork is torsionally rigid.

The rear end was a stressed sheet steel structure built according to a patent previously taken out in my name and tested on an MSS. This component, beside supporting the crew contained compartments for the battery and tools and also embodied upper mountings for the springs. To compensate for varying loads their upper ends could be moved forwards or backwards in curved slots, another of my own inventions which was subsequently employed on the LE and other post-war models.

When it finally got on the road, the "O" was not altogether an unqualified success. It would start at the brush of a carpet slipper, was as smooth as we hoped it would be, was very quiet mechanically and was completely oil-tight. But the gear change was clunky, the clutch was only just up to the job and the engine tightened up if driven at over 90 downhill.

Nothing much could be done about the clunk but increasing the plates from two to three cured the clutch trouble and increasing the sump capacity cured the partial seizures which were due to most of the oil being held up in the crankcase at high revs. After these modificatios and an alteration to the head angle to improve the high-speed navigation, the bike became a very relaxing, comfortable mount capable of around 95 m.p.h. (153 km.h) and a cruising consumption better than 60 m.p.g. If anyone wants confirmation, Frank Musset, who did a lot of test riding, will doubtless be happy to oblige. He might even tell you about the time he was stranded way down in Kent when some teeth fell out of the pair of coupling gears which were being tried in place of the originals which were promptly put back again.

Unfortunately, the outbreak of war stopped all further development and the "O" was used as a hack machine for several subsequent years by which time the factory was up to its ears in tooling up for the LE and building singles to keep the pot boiling. Whether it could be successful if re-introduced with some modern forks and styling features added is a point which would cost a lot of money to settle expecially as it would start with a handicap of not being a product made East of Suez.

15. THE CYCLONE

O ne of the unusual features of the Ducati 90 degree V-twin is the multiplicity of the bevel gears in the overhead camshaft drives, adding up to a total of nine.

Complexity of this nature is an accepted feature of modern motorcylces but contrary to what younger riders may think, the V-twin Cyclone, built in the USA *circa* 1915, also had its camshafts overhead and they too were driven by a number of bevels but arranged somewhat differently from the Ducati.

In the latter, a short bevel-driven shaft turns the front and rear vertical shafts by means of an intermediate bevel gear but in the Cyclone, the short shaft is not present.

The Cyclone overhead valve gear was not, of course, of the desmodromic variety, but it anticipated the design of the o.h.c. Velocette when this first came out in 1925. In both, the valve springs and the outer arms of the rockers were exposed to the air and any dust that it happened to contain, but the inner rocker arms and the camshaft were contained in a housing for lubrication and protection.

An interesting point of difference is that the Cyclone rockers did not bear directly on the valve stems, but had forked ends acting against stirrups, which extended about half way down the valve springs. This was probably done to reduce side-thrust on the valves from the rockers which was a contributary cause of rapid wear when the stems and guides were unlubricated but it also reduced the height of the camboxes.

Having adopted bevel-drive direct to a half-speed vertical shaft, and 1 to 1 bevels for the front camshaft, the designer was carried away with the idea, and not only drove the rear camshaft by bevels, but also incorporated two

The "Cyclone" was built by the Joern Motor Co. in St Paul U.S.A. between 1913 and 1920. Besides its O.H.C. engine it had a rear suspension system using a quarter-elliptic leaf spring clamped to the down-tubes which would probably be prone to fracture.

Right: In some respects the 1918 Cyclone was well a-head of its contemporaries but was a trifle more complex in its timing gear than the modern Ducati. The rocking stirrups on the valves reduced side thrust on the stems and also lowered the camshafts.

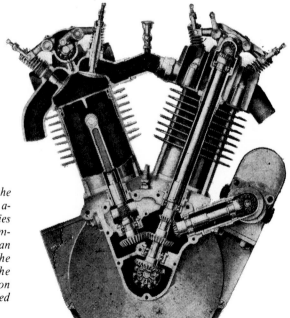

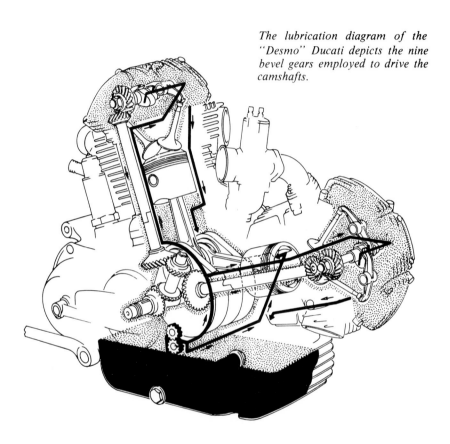

The lubrication diagram of the "Desmo" Ducati depicts the nine bevel gears employed to drive the camshafts.

more pairs to drive the magneto via an inclined shaft, making a grand total of six pairs. Getting all these to mesh correctly must have been an assembler's nightmare, unless the crankcase machining and gear-cutting were of a very high standard of accuracy.

Velocette was up against this problem with only two pairs of bevels in the KSS. The time taken to ensure that they would run without emitting a whine at high speed or clattering at low speed, plus the initial cost of the gears which were made by an outside firm, contributed to the model being eventually dropped.

Whether the illustration of the Cyclone is a photograph of a real sectioned engine or an artist's impression is not known, but it does depict some good features as well as some bad ones. The barrel finning is moderately deep and the detachable heads are held down by four long bolts, while the large inclined valves are installed at a favourable angle. On the other hand, the head finning is scanty, the ports are badly shaped, and the compression ratio appears to be not much more than 4 to 1.

The low octane rating of the petrol which was available at the time precluded the use of high compression, but in this instance, the shape of the chamber, the hot surfaces of the poorly-cooled head, and the thin cast-iron piston crown would be conducive to bad detonation whatever the ratio.

Downstairs, all bearings, including the big-ends, ran on rollers and there were also two mechanical oil-pumps, so the motor should have been able to compete with the contemporary Harleys, Indians, Excelsiors and so forth, which were technically less advanced. Seemingly not many were made and practically none exist today.

16. THE FOUR-CYLINDER WINDHOF

I t is always a pleasant change to look back at some long-forgotten motor-cycles which had plenty of promise or contained many advanced ideas but never got to the stage of being produced in any sizeable quantities.

At one time many factories were prepared to try out all sorts of ideas, some of which might have succeeded if better materials had been available at the time. On the other hand, some were doomed to failure at the start or were too advanced to be accepted except by a few enthusiasts.

One very interesting model which fits into the last category is the Windhof; built in Germany in 1928 by a factory which had previously depended on conventional machines with smaller two-stroke engines for its bread and butter.

The heart of this new and very ambitious model was a 750cc, four-cylinder engine with its three-bearing crankshaft lying fore and aft. Transverse engines of this size, were unknown at the time and in any case would rightly have been considered too wide.

The Windhof embodied many ideas which were not at all common at that period. For one thing it was "oversquare" — the dimensions being 63mm bore by 60mm stroke. And for another, it had vertical over-head valves operated directly by a single chain-driven camshaft.

All the rotating parts except the camshaft ran on ball or roller bearings and in general the specifications would conform well with all modern standards except for cooling the engine by oil. This was probably done to circumvent the overheating problem with the middle cylinders of an in-line four, but was an odd choice because the Windhof Company originally made radiators for cars and its first motorcycles were water-cooled two-strokes. The company thus knew a bit about the pros and cons of water-cooling and possibly the cons outweighed the pros in its opinion, and they went about the oil cooling system very thoroughly.

The oil which did double duty as a lubricant and a coolant was carried in a two gallon (9 litre) sump and the bulk of it was circulated by pump through the cylinder head and down through the jackets in the one-piece block

The head, block and sump were very liberally finned to dissipate heat, and in this respect the engine was a big improvement on the "oil boilers" designed by Granville Bradshaw with only a few fins on the cylinder head and none at all on the jacket and the crankcase.

The power from this interesting but expensive engine was transmitted through a multi-plate clutch to a three-speed hand-change gearbox bolted to the rear of the crankcase. The kick start, of the folding pattern, was mounted on the box and moved in the conventional direction insead of transversely as on the BMW so it must have turned the engine through bevel gearing.

From the gearbox the power went by an open propeller shaft to a worm driven rear axle. The overall gear ratios were 4.3, 6 and 10 to 1, a well spaced set which should have provided effortless cruising with the big wheels then in vogue.

There was no frame at all in the conventional sense. Instead, a massive steering-head casting was bolted to the front end of the engine and a three gallon (13.6 litre) petrol tank sat directly on the camshaft cover.

At the rear, four parallel steel bars extended from the unit above and below the gearbox to castings on each side of the rear wheel, one of which comprised the worm drive housing.

Contrary to modern practice, but commonplace at the time, this rear wheel was quickly detachable, the operation being assisted by a hinged rear mudguard and a roll-on centre stand. Also, the brake was not in the hub, retardation being supplied by a transmission brake on the propeller shaft adjacent to the gearbox.

The front suspension was provided by a fork with short trailing bottom links connected to a single leaf spring by a "U" shaped member operated in tension. The design was not unlike the suspension systems used by Indian and BMW of about the same vintage, but the bottom links also acted as friction dampers and the handle-bars, attached to the crown, were adjustable for angle.

If this bike was available today I'll bet some oaf would be riding around with the bars pointing straight up in the air!

The electrical system was quite lavish, sparks being provided by a magneto driven from the camshaft and nestling just below the saddle which itself was pivoted to the rear of the tank.

The battery sat between the saddle springs, well up out of harm's way, but the large headlight and electric horn, were mounted on the forks — a little too far forward of the steering column for ease of handling.

Top: This view of the Windhof clearly shows the horizontal steel bars forming the rear forks, and the roll-on central stand.

Centre: Underside of the cylinder head with passages for the oil used for cooling.

Above: The power unit is the main structural member to which all the other components are attached.

Other features worthy of note were the sensible mudguards at both ends, the uncluttered exhaust system, the luggage carrier and large hollow footboards which also acted as tool-boxes. All in all except for the lack of rear springing, the specification indicated a lot of forward thinking and some excellent features . . . and some not so good.

Accessibility must have been of a low order, but on the other hand not much routine maintenance should have been required. Nevertheless, the model had only a short production life being superseded after a couple of years by a totally different design with a 1000cc side-valve, flat-twin engine. This unit had shaft drive and a pressed steel frame which could have resembled a BMW of the period.

There must have been some reasons for the limited life of the four cylinder model other than its price which was somewhat higher than usual. Maybe the concept was too advanced to find much public support but in all probability the cause lay in the oil cooling system.

Engine oil is not nearly so effective as water as a cooling medium. It will absorb heat quite readily but does not like giving it up again. In extreme conditions water can get rid of heat from hot-spots very quickly by local boiling, but besides having a much higher boiling point oil is liable to form carbonaceous deposits on high-temperature surfaces, thereby blocking up the passages and diverting more of the oil to other areas which, being cooler, do not need any more oil, but reducing the flow to the places where it is needed most urgently. Also, the horizontal fins, while being effective at speed would be of little use in traffic or when pulling up hill even when they were clean. It would not be very long before they would clog up with mud on anything but sealed surfaces and this would ruin the cooling entirely.

If a conventional water cooling system had been adopted in the first place it is possible that the model would have remained in production for much longer. But the whole design would have had to be modified considerably to permit the installation of a radiator without it projecting by an amount which is acceptable today but would have been considered impractically wide at the time.

Maybe there were other reasons which collectively led to the abandonment, but that does not alter the fact that in many ways the design was technically outstanding and well in advance of most of its contemporaries.

17. NAME-PLATE LOYALTY

The term "name-plate loyalty" was coined long ago in America to describe the attitude of riders towards the particular make of machine they favored for every-day use or rode in competition either as amateurs or professionals on the factory payrolls.

If you were a Harley man or an Indian man or one who preferred a less illustrious make of machine, you stuck to it year after year, stoutly defending your choice agains the slurs thrown at it by riders sufficiently misguided to favor different machinery.

In return of course you treated their mounts with scorn and derision even though you knew in your innermost heart that your remarks were a bit below the belt.

P. C. Vincent discovered just how strong this name plate loyalty was and its affect on sales in the USA when the Vincent HRD was introduced to that country in 1946. To the American mind a big V-twin just had to be a Harley or an Indian, all other domestic models having disappeared, and those who preferred big machines would not do violence to their loyalties by purchasing one of another brand even though the local products were far too heavy and could not match the performance of the Vincent HRD.

Even when Rollie Free lifted the U.S. speed record from 143 to 159m.p.h. many riders were under the impression that this feat was accomplished on a Harley Davidson, or HD as the motorcycling papers termed it. In fact this misconception was one of the reasons why the letters HRD were dropped from the trade mark, which became simply "Vincent" in 1948.

Where professional riders were concerned, most of them remained faithful to one chosen make for year after year even though getting the pants beaten off them time after time.

In earlier days, if you were a Harley man, you were a Harley man through hell or high water. Loyalty to your particular brand of machine meant almost as much as having a feed.

Instead of rushing off and getting one of the successful models they kept plugging on with their own and frequently got back to the winner's circle. Of course, at the time the riders were usually employed by the factories and only a handful of special racing models were built, so it wasn't very easy to swap over from one make to another. But even if it had been, loyalty in most cases would have prevented it.

In this way top-line riders became identified with their machines and gained large numbers of enthusiastic followers in consequence.

Men like Jim Davis and Paul Anderson, for instance, will always be remembered for their performances on Indian while Ralph Hepburn's name was synonymous with Harleys for years until he came to Australia. Then he changed over to AJS as the 350cc Harley Pea-shooter had not then appeared.

Name-plate loyalty was by no means confined to the States. It existed everywhere else and led to the formation of "one-make" clubs, expecially in Australia.

The five clubs which originally formed the Auto-Cycle Union of Victoria were all of this variety and the club members who were prominent in competitions remained faithful to one make even though not always successful.

One advantage of this was that if a rider who had made a name for himself went over to England, he was assured of a good reception by the makers of the machine he favoured.

I even landed a job at Velocette partly on the strength of having won a few grass-track races on a tuned-up KSS, and Frank Mussett was also a popular visitor to the Hall Green factory especially at T.T. periods.

TT riders were specially notable for their adherence to one make although as the number of factories entering dwindled, many perforce had to make a change.

The Rudge trio of Graham Walker, Ernie Nott and Tyrell Smith failed to score a win until 1930 when they got into the groove and won many races in the next couple of years until Rudge officially pulled out for financial reasons. The three then formed a syndicate, bought their mounts from the factory and financed themselves in 1933, unfortunately with little success.

Of recent day successful riders, Roger De Coster is one of the few who have stuck with one company for any great period of time. And his time with Suzuki has rewarded him with great success though we can wonder that if Suzuki's success had waned for a year or so would he have stayed.

Multi-Australian moto-cross champion Trevor Flood has continued to have success throughout the years despite continually playing a game of "musical motorcycles".

Tyrell Smith joined Excelsior in 1936 when Alan Bruce, from Melbourne, was in charge of the racing department and he rode nothing else until the outbreak of war.

Another staunch one-make man was George Rowley who piloted AJS machines exclusively and almost continuously for 14 years. Norton riders like Jimmy Guthrie, Freddie Frith or "Crasher" White naturally stayed with a winning camp but Stanley Woods, who also rode Nortons, was inclined to appear, and win, on other makes like Velocette or Guzzi.

After the war, motorcycle racing was in a rather depressed state as many factories were either war-weary, bombed out of existence or carted off holus-bolus to Russia.

There were more good riders than there were mounts for them to ride. This led to a lot of reshuffling and many top-line English riders were engaged mainly by Italian firms to develop road-racing models which were very fast but handled badly. They naturally got money for this job but not a great deal by today's standards. Honda brought about big changes in this regard, in 1960.

Its own nationals not being then over-brilliant in the saddle, Honda raked in men like Hailwood, McIntyre and anyone else that could be recruited regardless of expense until there were so many good riders in its team that no other make had a look-in.

Not all the men remained with Honda, but Tom Phillis who was employed as a full-time development rider, did so until he died in the 1960 Junior TT while trying hard on a model which did not have a cat's chance anyway.

By that time, all the Japanese racing factories had got in on the act and with their huge domestic sales and increasing exports, had enough money to hire any riders they wanted. Cash rather than loyalty decided who would ride what until the factories began to prune their expenditure, and Honda pulled out altogether.

A new feature then began to creep in. This was in the form of sponsorship by firms who were not necessarily associated with the motorcycle industry but merely wished to use the machines as mobile billboards, plastered from stem to stern with advertising material. Some firms even went as far as to supply finance on a big scale for development purposes but most were content to pay out smaller amounts just for the publicity which they gained, win or lose. As a result, nameplate loyalty just about disappeared, riders being content or forced to shop around for as much money as they could get, and having got it purchased a set of flamboyant leathers with their name down one leg and the sponsor's down the other. Even a mediocre person could become an immediate big-time racer without the necessity of risking his neck trying to beat better men.

Naturally a sponsor would rather be on a winner than a loser and as Yamahas became very difficult to beat, more and more people opted to use them, until eventually most races became one-make benefits not because of loyalty to the make but simply for financial reasons.

From the aspect of motorcycle sport, this is not a praiseworthy situation.

18. FUEL CONSUMPTION

W hatever happened to fuel consumption? There's one obvious answer to this question: it went sky-high about 15 years ago and has remained so ever since, despite wails about the ever-rising cost of petrol and the pleas of the clean-air lobby.

A more interesting matter is why it went that way without much protest from either the public or the press. While most test reports and some readers' letters will devote a vitriolic paragraph or two to the poor location of a switch, or some such piffling detail that an owner could rectify for himself, the matter of fuel consumption is often not referred to at all, or — if unusually excessive — may be dismissed with a few mildly critical words, instead of being roundly condemned under a sub-heading such as "Atrocious Fuel Consumption".

Unfortunately, the picture has lately become somewhat obscured by supplanting our time-honoured and well-understood system of reckoning consumption in miles per gallon, indicating how far you can go on a known amount of fuel, by the system of stating how many litres are used in covering 100 kilometres.

Though it uses metric units, litres per 100 kilometres is not really a metric system but a French idea which, to me, seems back-to-front, and is not easily compared to consumptions recorded on the old system.

However, I did not set out to complain about the metric system being shoved down our throats, but to discuss why motorcycles, with a few exceptions, have ceased to be the economical vehicles which they were once.

The chief offenders, judged on a size-for-size basis, are small-capacity Japanese two-strokes, which can consume fuel almost as rapidly as a small car. There was a time when a 250 could cover twice or thrice the distance per unit of petrol than a modern example will, though the former would not have had anything like as good a performance. But in those days, performance did not matter very much. If you wanted more speed, you purchased a bigger machine and, even then, the increased consumption would probably still be less than the present-day standards which most riders seem prepared to accept.

Symptomatic of this acceptance of a bad situation is the emphasis continually placed by writers and advertisers on methods and equipment for improving the factory speed performance; very rarely do you come across an article or product intended to improve consumption!

The inference of this is that only a small minority are really interested in running costs or distance between re-fills, and certainly not to the extent of spending a few dollars in order to save a much larger number of cents in the future.

This attitude might be partly because most motorcycles are only ridden for short distances; for long distances the owner goes by car, or takes the bike on a trailer. Because the total usage of fuel is not very great, the fact that it is being used uneconomically escapes notice.

The major factor contributing to this situation is the worship of high-speed performance, regardless of almost every other attribute that a good machine should possess. The only way to get a high power output from a smallish engine is by running it at very high rpm, but unfortunately this can only be achieved at the expense of losing low and then middle-range torque, and using up much more fuel irrespective of whether the bike is driven hard or just pottered around in towns.

This is so because the port timings and areas necessary for high two-stroke power at speeds approaching 10,000 rpm are such that at lower speeds much of the fresh mixture goes out unburned through the exhaust port and is wasted. Worse still, instead of pulling strongly almost down to walking pace, which was a characteristic of the older two-bangers, the modern ones drop their bundle at 4000 or 5000 revs, due to the pressure waves in the exhaust and transfer systems, getting out of phase, and have to be kept on the boil by continually changing down as the road speed drops. Naturally, the consumption suffers.

At very high speeds, a fair amount of power is required merely to overcome internal friction and to pump combustion air through the cylinders which can be appreciated from the braking effect evident when running downhill in low gear with the ignition switched off and the throttle alternately opened and closed. The power thus absorbed can only be derived from part of the fuel used.

A severe lack of low-speed torque also means that bottom gear must be quite low for starting off, and then five or even six ratios are essential to make the machine rideable on winding roads or hilly country, and very frequent gear-changing is necessary. A citizen who rides one of these screamers through my village about 10 times a day never seems to go for more than five seconds before changing up or down.

Lately there have been welcome signs that some factories are changing their thinking — for example, by using reed valves to stop the blowback which causes loss of fuel — but, nevertheless, it would be better if they places less emphasis on high performance and brought some semblance of sanity into the consumption question before petrol prices rise still higher and emission controls get tougher.

Four-stroke engines have also suffered from the high-output high-rev syndrome, with touring tachometers red-lined at speeds which not so long ago would be considered too fast even for a racer. Fortunately, being less dependent than two-strokes on wave action in the breathing and exhaust departments, the bottom end does not fall out of the power curve quite so distressingly and driveability is better, but still the consumption is often very excessive.

For example, the CJ250T Honda twin recently was tested in Australia and with a maximum speed of 134 km/h (84 mph) had an overall consumption of 5 litres per 100 kilometres, equal to only 54 mpg, but a pre-World War II Speed Twin 500 cm^3 Triumph weighing much the same would go as fast or even faster while returning about 15 percent better consumption.

This is because the Triumph was not intended to run above 6000 rpm and the valve-timing and pipe sizes were designed for maximum torque of around 4000 with good flexibility and economy, whereas the Honda engine of half the capacity has to turn nearly twice as fast to develop about the same power, while the valve timing and breathing arrangements have to be tailored for high-speed performance at the expense of other qualities.

One of the latest examples of Oriental ingenuity, the XS750-D Yamaha, is clearly intended to be a fast tourer rather than a road-equipped racer, but falls down in the very department in which it should excel. A recent tester was impelled to register a protest — a mild one, but nevertheless a protest — against a consumption almost equalled that of a small car, but charitably ascribed it to an over-rich setting of one of the three carburettors.

Without giving any other reason, it was felt that the test machine was not a typical example, because a figure of 7 litres per 100 kilometres was expected, and presumably would have been accepted without comment! Even at cruising speed, the consumption exceeded this figure, reducing the tank range to 200 kilometres so an extra fuel supply would be essential in many country areas.

Again going back a few years, the 1000 cm^3 Vincent Rapide, with a higher maximum than the Yamaha, would easily record 60 mpg (4.7 litres per 100 kilometres) at a fast touring clip even on a compression ratio low enough to use 70 octane petrol, and a careful rider could get close to 70 mpg (4.0 litres per 100 kilometres). One only has to look at the transmission systems and top-gear ratio of the two machines to see some reasons why this should be.

The XS750-D Yamaha's power is transmitted in all ratios through a total of five steps, which are all less than 100 percent efficient, but when in top gear the big twin's power only goes through two chains, with less power loss for the majority of running, but the real reason lies in the top gear ratios of 5.2 to 1 for the Yamaha and 3.5 to 1 for the Rapide.

When doing the "ton", the twin was only burbling round at 4600 rmp while the three-cylinder model is running at 7000 and using up a lot of its fuel just in spinning itself around.

At lower speeds, it loses out for other reasons and there does not seem to be much point in providing double overhead camshafts, multiple carburettors and so forth for a machine which is neither outstandingly fast nor economical, when it could quite easily be one or the other depending on the aim of the designer.

19. FASHIONS IN TANKS

Originally, most motorcycle fuel tanks were slab-sided angular affairs, remarkable more for their utility than their beauty. Besides holding petrol, they frequently had a compartment for oil, which was fed to the engine by a hand-pump. They also formed a handy mounting-place for the gear-lever quadrant and other levers operating the ignition advance or clutch.

Being the largest object to which rudimentary styling could be applied, it was not long before tanks became more shapely, and were painted and decorated according to the makers' tastes, each adopting and retaining an individual style so that one make could be distinguished from others by the look of its tank, just the same as for many years cars were mainly recognised by the shapes of their radiators.

The usual location was between the upper and lower frame tubes, the lower tube being often referred to as the tank-rail. While this was good enough for small capacities, the tank had to be made excessively wide if a big capacity was required.

To obviate this, the Americans introduced the pannier construction, in which the tank was made in two complete halves, each higher than the top tube, which was sandwiched in between. This had the merit that one side could be used as a reserve supply, and a leaky or damaged half could be run empty until it could be repaired.

Leaky or split tanks were not uncommon, partly because of the method of construction, but more because it was usual to bolt the tank rigidly to the frame, so that it was subjected to high-speed vibrations from the engine and to strains caused by flexing of the frame.

Some makers continued to use a compartment for oil instead of a separate tank, and a leakage could be a serious matter if it allowed petrol to get into the oil, the usual result being a seized engine.

The tank on this very carly Indian racing machine was fitted between the frame tubes and retained by clips. Note the absence of saddle springs.

Consequently, the idea lost favour, but we had to resort to it in the pre-war Series "A" Vincent-HRD Rapide, which was so compact that there was no room to install a separate oil-tank in the conventional position.

While some English factories adopted the pannier style, others favoured the saddle tank, which had a large central channel fitting over the top tube. The tank rail was no longer required as a support, and was eventually omitted to the advantage of the frame, as one large tube is lighter and has more torsional rigidity than two small ones.

The tank could then be fixed to the head lug and saddle lug with rubber blocks or bushes interposed to protect it from engine vibration or frame stresses.

By this time, the tankside gear lever was on its way to oblivion, following on the invention of the Velocette foot change. The other levers had gone years ago, and there was nothing to stop the tank being any shape or size the designer wished. George Brough took full advantage of this with the large shapely bulbous tank on the Brough Superior, a trend which was quickly followed in other big machines.

It was a common practice to protect the tank enamel with soft rubber knee-pads, a sensible practice which has now gone by the board. The stately black enamel with gold lining — considered the acme of good taste — gradually gave way to more eye-catching finishes with large areas of chrome-plating, but a lavish display of bright colours was less popular then than it is now.

From time to time, someone would come along with a design in which the tank actually formed part of the frame.

Tankside levers as shown here disappeared after gear-changing by foot became universal.

The Beardmore-Precision was a good example of this construction, which at first glance appears to have some merit, but was never widely adopted.

It has to be made in thicker steel than a separate tank, and has to be welded to lugs or tubes at front and rear, leaving nooks and crannies which are difficult to de-scale and were not always petrol-tight. Also, if the capacity was big, the non-removable feature made the top half of the engine inaccessible for routine maintenance.

The pressing need to reduce pit-stop times in long-distance races led to the old screw-cap being replaced by quick-action caps, which could be opened in one movement, remaining attached while the fuel was poured in and then shut with equal speed.

One of the best was an Italian design, in which the opening and closing movements were performed by a lever easily moved with a gloved hand. This type was very popular for racing and sports models, but was a little too expensive and not neat enough for bread-and-butter models.

Welded aluminium tanks came into use for racing back in 1932, but were not entirely split-proof because really reliable welding alloys had not been developed. Nevertheless, they gave good service if properly rubber-mounted and were lighter than steel ones. But their use was confined to racing.

New Imperial struck a new note on the 500 cm³ twin-cylinder model by using magnesium with the joints made by rivetting on the de Bergue system developed for aircraft tanks, a very expensive but reliable method of manufacture.

The large ungainly tank on the 1948 Senior Moto-Guzzi surrounded the steering column and was shaped to fit the rider's elbows and knees.

108

The Featherbed frame, designed by R. and C. McCandles in Belfast and adopted by Joe Craig for Nortons, had two parallel tubes at approximately bottom tank level and the construction and mounting of the tank was simplified and improved by sitting it on these tubes with sponge-rubber insulation and holding it down by a single central strap.

Then someone else found that it is not necessary to hold the tank down by mechanical methods; a couple of stout rubber bands at each end were sufficient until the machine is crashed, whereupon the tank is likely to go off into its own orbit.

When the LE Velocette, which I was involved with design-wise, was in the pencil-and-paper stage, it was decided to substitute the traditional attractive but costly tank by a more mundane article hidden from sight inside the pressed-steel frame. Where the tank would otherwise have been, we incorporated a compartment to hold gloves or other bric-a-brac, for which there is never any accommodation provided.

The filler-cap was easily accessible but, with a consumption of around 90m.p.g. (3 litres per 100 km), it did not need to be used very often, and the tank was high enough to retain gravity feed.

A concealed tank of rather complicated shape is used on the GL 1000 Honda, a mechanical fuel pump being required because its bottom is lower than the carburettors.

This early racing Moto-Guzzi carried its oil in a separate tank fixed on top of the main fuel reservoir.

The small filler cap is located beneath a hinged lid on a glass-fibre container resembling a saddle tank in appearance, but this lid has a coin-slot type of catch at the rear-most end, so the filling process with cold wet hands would seem to be unnecessarily irksome.

This idea of concealing the filler-cap appears to be a growing fashion, which has very little to recommend it and certainly is not a feature that would appeal to all-weather riders.

Glass-fibre came into use some years ago for production tanks and, though satisfactory for normal work, was legally banned in England following some bad fires caused by the tanks splitting or disintegrating as the result of a fall or collision.

However, it is handy stuff for making special tanks on a one-off or limited production basis, and is often employed for combined seat and tail tank units on racing two-strokes, which require a lot of tank space owing to the high rate at which they burn up the contents.

The 1974 model four-cylinder Suzuki needed no less than 38 litres to cover three laps of the 60-kilometres Isle of Man TT course without re-fuelling.

The sheer size of the Suzuki tank was obviously uncomfortable for the rider, while the huge weight of fuel affected both handling and accelerating adversely in the early stages. In fact, 22 litres is about the maximum which can conveniently be carried.

Reduction of weight is very important on a trail bike, but some standard tanks are so pitifully small that spare petrol must be carried on mountain runs, and it is lighter overall to put the whole lot into one sensibly-sized tank.

20. PROBLEMS ON THE TRAILS

When a small section of a minority group begins to aggravate the rest of society, by the careless, thoughtless, or even dangerous activities of its members, all sorts of organizations from the government down to local committees composed mainly of self-appointed guardians are likely to be stirred into action.

This usually starts off with vocal objections or letters to the papers by the less-exalted bodies, which have no power to do anything more than grumble loudly, but if the offenders have any sense they should give some heed to the fulminations against them by voluntarily curtailing their activities — or at least doing something to reduce the annoyance to an acceptable level. Otherwise, bodies which do possess legal powers to control or limit the actions of citizens will begin to take official notice or even enact restrictive measures which, once instituted, take a lot of repealing.

In Australia, besides Federal and State governments and local councils whose members depend upon public goodwill at election times, there are other statutory bodies such as the Environment Protection Society, the Forestry Department, and the conservationists whose positions are not affected by the whims of the electorate, and between them they wield a tremendous amount of power to influence legislation. This may have the desired effect of abating a nuisance, but almost invariably does so by also limiting the actions of other persons who have not been concerned in causing the trouble.

A case in point is the outcry against trailbikes and their minibike brothers, or to be more accurate against some of the riders of these machines.

Trailbikes are all very well in their way, and are useful for jobs like rounding up stock or getting into places where a four wheeler is too big to go, but

thousands of them are used only for fun which seems to consist largely of tearing up and down almost unclimbable hills and making a hellish din which echoes round the mountains and can be heard sometimes a great distance away. In many places, knobbly tyres on spinning wheels have cut grooves in the soil which in wet country are very likely to form runnels that eventually become deep washaways. In sandy soil, especially on dunes exposed to sea breezes, a track cut through the thin vegetation can become a deep blow-out, and evidence of this can be seen all along our coastline wherever there are dunes to be climbed — for no good purpose except to come down again, put the bike on a trailer and motor off back home, after having frightened almost to death every living thing in the area.

Part of the annoyance caused by these models is that they are based on machines which have been developed for cross-country competitions and in

This pic clearly shows the extent the authorities are going to now in Australia to dissuade off-road vehicles from harming the environment.

today's idiom this means a high-revving, low-geared two-stroke with a raucous exhaust system which gives good top-end power, but so little low speed torque that it has to be ridden hard all the time. There is no plonking slowly up a hill with the minimum amount of noise or wheelspin like Sammy Miller used to do on his single-cylinder four-stroke Ariel — but there are no machines equivalent to that one, or to the BSA Victor, on the market today. The nearest equivalent is the Yamaha XT500, but with four valves and an overhead camshaft, it is more complicated and more difficult for a private owner to work on than the once-popular push-rod big singles which most young riders have never owned or even ridden.

It is true that recently some two-strokes, mostly of European origin, have been partly detuned and made more tractable, and some local firms can supply exhaust systems giving improved tractability at some sacrafice in speed, but there are a large number of models existing which cannot be made either tractable or silent because of their exaggerated port timing.

We're faced with the fact that something pretty drastic in the way of limiting the use, noise and damage caused by trailbikes has to be done and if it is not done voluntarily, it will be done compulsorily. The writing is on the wall in the form of Acts of Parliament relating to the use of what are called "recreational vehicles" in certain areas and the closing of many bush tracks to traffic. Unofficial action has been taken in some places by stringing nylon fishing line, or even in one instance barbed wire across trails which are repeatedly traversed at high speed by unwelcome visitors on two wheels. Bush walkers or less dedicated souls who use such tracks as normal pathways, are naturally annoyed at finding them chopped up into bogs by knobbly tyres, and while there is no real excuse for retaliatory actions which will almost certainly cause injury and perhaps death, the reasons prompting the actions are easily understood.

In my opinion, the motorcycling journals are not entirely free from blame. Continually emphasizing the spectacular side of trail-riding in words and pictures, they are full of scenes depicting intrepid riders leaping high in the air over a hillcrest, or about to touch down after a wheelstand, thereby giving young and inexperienced riders the impression that it is all very easy and perfectly safe. Little or nothing is said about the risks involved in trying to emulate the skill of the professional trail rider or about riding methods which will give the least possible annoyance to others who live in or pass through the vicinity.

All the animosity is by no means caused by single-track machines. In the past year or so four-wheel-drive vehicles have come under heavy attack, especially by bush-walkers who every now and again have to be rescued by the very vehicles they are objecting to. Landrovers and Jeeps have been in use for a long time without causing much complaint in forest and desert areas, but of late, smaller four-wheel-drive vehicles have been extensively advertized as go-anywhere, do-anything "fun" machines. They command ready sales, but are not always used in a manner which is acceptable to others.

114

The growing popularity of off-road racing as an officially-recognized and promoted sport is also going to meet with considerable opposition if allowed to proliferate, or if several hundred machines are permitted to start in one event, especially in some districts where the ecology is so finely balanced that extensive damage to the terrain will have permanent effects on the native flora and fauna.

If or when more laws are passed restricting off-road activity it will be very difficult to rescind them, and once again, a large number of people will suffer from the actions of a few.

21. ONE OF MOTORCYCLING'S GREATS

Not many T.T. winners become successful journalists. Fewer still rise to be the Editor of a motorcycling periodical of international renown. But there was one unforgettable character who achieved both distinctions, a feat which is never likely to be duplicated. That remarkable man was, of course, the late Graham Walker.

Graham had gone into motorcycling the hard way, as a despatch rider in the first war, in which his left ankle was so badly damaged that it was thought he would be unable to ride a motorcycle and was awarded a pension. He then found that he could ride quite well, informed the authorities of that fact, but they insisted on paying the pension just the same!

After competing in the T.T. since 1920 and coming fairly close to winning a few times on Norton and Sunbeam machines, Graham scored a victory in the Lightweight T.T. on a 250 Rudge. He had changed over to this make in 1928 after Sunbeam had dropped out of the running, but being a large type, more heavily built than his team mates, H. G. Tyrell-Smith and Ernie Nott, he preferred the Junior and Senior models. Deciding to ride the little machine in 1931, he brought it home to a very popular win ahead of Tyrell-Smith, Ernie Nott having retired.

After some very fruitful years, Rudge-Whitworth could not put up with the heat, and officially withdrew from the racing kitchen. The three "works" riders then formed a syndicate, bought the racing machines and rode them on a shoestring budget without overmuch success until 1934 which was Graham's last T.T. season. He earned a third place in the Lightweight, and sixth in the Senior. Since 1927 he had never fallen and had never been off the leader board in any of his races.

Then, after four years as Rudge-Whitworth Competition Manager, he became Editor of "Motor Cycling" and set about re-vitalizing it to good effect, with the assistance of reporters such as Dennis May, Harvey Pascoe, Alec Menhinnick and Bernal Osborne. Sports coverage was increased, but the touring and technical aspects were not neglected. Graham roped me in as an outside contributor doing the Technical Reviews of the T.T. and motor-cycle shows, and also technical articles under the nom-de-plume of "Slide Rule".

Then came the Second War. Graham collaborated with the War Office in forming a Despatch Riders Training Scheme, but also lost most of his staff. However he kept the flag flying, even when London was falling to bits round his ears when the V2 rockets started to come over. His old staffmen sent in stuff when they could. I kept up my contributions and Joe Craig supplied many admirable articles on Norton racing development. To keep things going I weighed in with a repair series under the name Tinker, and towards the end of the war, Graham suggested to me that a tuning series might help the lads returning home. These articles appeared for a couple of years, and were eventually combined into "Tuning for Speed".

All this time Graham was doing a lot of his own reporting and whenever he heard of a new design or invention he would hare up to the factory concerned to find out what lay behind the rumour. I remember him coming up to Velocette twice, once to have a ride on an MSS with adjustable rear springing, and then to examine the geared-twin Model O, but he never allowed anything to be published until the date set by the manufacturer. Conversely, he maintained that pandering to the wishes of big-spending advertisers, even indirectly or by inference, lowered the prestige and reputation of the paper and he steadfastly refused to alter his editorial policy or retract any fair, but unfavourable comments made by the staff in road tests. Occasional threats to cancel advertising agreements were ignored and oddly enough, were never implemented.

When peace broke out, Graham was a tired man, living in a changed world, but the return of some of the old hands eased his burden somewhat. When racing resumed on a reduced scale, with petrol limited to 70 octane, he maintained the sports coverage as well as he could and also continued the job of broadcasting the commentaries on the T.T. races, where his detailed knowledge of the course made his commentaries come alive.

In his first post-war year of this task, disaster struck. Barrington, on a twin-cylinder Guzzi, was in the lead of the Lightweight class on the roads, and the privateer, Maurice Cann also Guzzi-mounted, was close behind on the roads, but actually in the lead on corrected time. He stopped to change a valve-spring on the second last lap, thereby losing the time lead but only by

Graham Walker — motorcyclist, T.T. winner, journalist, radio personality and a very courteous gentleman whose death was universally deplored.

two seconds. Coming into the finish a hundred stop-watches clicked as Barrington crossed the line, and clicked again as Cann followed, 16 seconds later, thus apparently winning by 16 seconds, allowing for the starting interval. Graham, up in the broadcasting box, has also been clicking his stopwatch, and announced that Cann was the winner, only to be dumbfounded by a message from the timekeepers that Barrington had won by 44 seconds! Graham just would not accept this verdict nor did many others, as it seemed that somehow an extra minute had been tacked on to Cann's last lap time, which was recorded as being 10 seconds slower than his fill-up lap. Uproar, protests and demands for a recount all failed to move the timekeepers to alter their decision, and Barrington went into the records as the winner.

Graham continued his broadcasting for many years, but gradually relinquished his control of "Motorcycling", becoming Consulting Editor while R. R. Holliday became the executive editor. When Lord Montague decided to form a motorcycle section at the Beaulieu Motor Museum, Graham was appointed Curator and took up residence with his wife, Elsie, in a very ancient building in the grounds of Beaulieu Abbey, where I stayed for a weekend or two. On the last visit we dragged out "Old Miracle", the single-geared Norton on which D. R. O'Donovan established many records, and rode it round the drives, which was an unforgettable experience — but not as unforgettable as the man who brought it about.

22. SOME SIGNS I HAVE SEEN.

Anyone who keeps his eyes open when travelling round his own and other countries will often find cause for some quiet mirth in signs and notices written evidently by people who did not realize that the words did not exactly mean what they were intended to say, or alternatively made a great fuss out of labouring the obvious. An example of the latter is a notice saying "Give Way to Trains" recently erected at all the hundreds of level crossings in Victoria. Surely nobody needs to be **warned** to allow a train the right-of-way?

Illustrated on these pages is just a small selection of genuine signs which I have observed in Australia and England. My favourite is the Motel toilet sign, photographed in Eucla, a remote settlement half way between Perth and Adelaide. Apart from the unconventional spelling the more one looks at it the more errors there are!

Some of them appeared first in "Motorcycle Action" and at least three have been re-worded since then. Is this coincidence or an example of the Power of the Press?

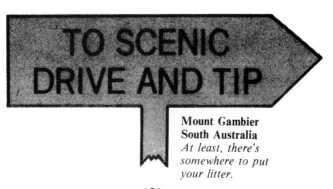

Mount Gambier
South Australia
*At least, there's
somewhere to put
your litter.*

**NO PARKING
AT ANY TIME
ON BOTH SIDES
OF THE ROAD
IN FRONT OF
FIRE STATION**

Warrandyte, Victoria
Work this one out!

**THIS BUS STOP
TEMPORARILY DISCONTINUED**

**Newton Abbot
England**
*Don't bother to
hail the bus.*

**LOOSE STONES
TRAVEL SLOWLY**

Road sign used in Victoria
*They travel fast enough to
break your windscreen.*

Sandown Race Course, Melbourne
Just could not keep his feet on the ground.

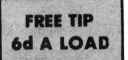

**Council Sign
Warwickshire**
*Well, is it
free or not?*

Notice in Motel Toilet, Eucla, West Australia
A bit difficult to comply with!

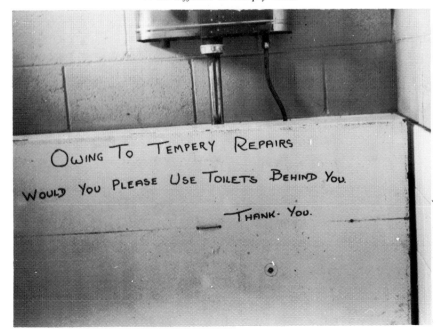

ILLEGAL
PARKING
PROHIBITED

Road sign, Sydney N.S.W.
What about legal parking?

**Warning notice
on service truck
Sydney Harbour
Bridge**

When does it move?

STOPPING
CONTINUOUSLY

Sign near Bunbury West Australia
What is the $40 for?

$40

A sign in West Australia
which should be heeded and not laughed at.

POLICE GENTLEMEN

**Street sign
Peterborough
South Australia**

Social Distinction?

**PERSONS IN THIS
BAR WILL NOT BE
SERVED LIQUOR
UNDER THE AGE
OF 18 YEARS**

Motor Show, Melbourne
Vintage port, perhaps

NO PARKING. NO STANDING. LIMIT 2 MINUTES

Parking Notice, Melbourne Airport
Pretty generous, really.

THIS GATE MUST
BE SHUT AT
ALL TIMES

Boundary Gate, Muloorina, South Australia
How are you supposed to go though it?

ROAD CLOSED 90
PENALTY $200
AIR AND GROUND PATROLS